Collins

SCIENCE PLUS

THIRD EDITION

G000135187

2

Approved publication

OCR

RECOGNISING ACHIEVEMENT

William Collins' dream of knowledge for all began with the publication of his first book in 1819. A self-educated mill worker, he not only enriched millions of lives, but also founded a flourishing publishing house. Today, staying true to this spirit, Collins books are packed with inspiration, innovation and practical expertise. They place you at the centre of a world of possibility and give you exactly what you need to explore it.

Collins. Freedom to teach.

Published by Collins
An imprint of HarperCollinsPublishers
77–85 Fulham Palace Road
Hammersmith
London
W6 8JB

Browse the complete Collins catalogue at
www.collinseducation.com

© HarperCollinsPublishers Limited 2006

10 9 8 7 6 5 4 3 2 1

ISBN-13 978-0-00-721649-9
ISBN-10 0-00-721649-1

British Library Cataloguing in Publication Data
A Catalogue record for this publication is available from the British Library

Commissioned by Kate Hayward and Cassandra Birmingham

Publishing Manager Michael Cotter

Project managed by Jennifer Carruth

Edited by Anita Clark

Cover design by John Fordham and Bob Lea

Internal design by JPD

Page make-up by JPD

Picture research by Caroline Thompson

Illustrations by IFADesign Ltd and JPD

Production by Natasha Buckland

Printed and bound by Martins the Printers, Berwick upon Tweed

Acknowledgements

Every effort has been made to contact the holders of copyright material, but if any have been inadvertently overlooked the publishers will be pleased to make the necessary arrangements at the first opportunity.

The publishers would like to thank the following for permission to reproduce photographs (T = Top, B = Bottom, C = Centre, L= Left, R = Right):

Ardea London Ltd/Valerie Taylor, p6;

ABPL/Gerrit Buntrock, p11, Graham Kirk, p25;

Cephas/Nigel Blythe, p20;

www.codetection.com, p65C;

Martyn Chillmaid, p7, p26, p28C&B, p60CT, p 65TR, p66, p70R, p72, p103;

Martyn Chillmaid/Carphone Warehouse, p104;

Corbis/ Mian Khursheed/Reuters, p41;

Courtesy of the Library of Congress, p8T;

Empics/David Cheskin/PA, p97;

FLPA/Nigel Cattlin, p22, p24C, p56L;

Getty Images, p13, Stone, p28T, p32, p55C;

Ronald Grant Archive/New Line Cinema, p21;

iStockphoto, p78;

©jonarnoldimages/Walter Bibikow, p37, Gavin Hellier, p53;

© 2006Jupiterimages Corporation, p50, p68, p110;

The Kobal Collection, p73T, Warner Bros, p12, 20th Century Fox, p47, Hammer/Warner Bros, p65TL, Touchstone / Masi, Frank, p79, Morgan Creek / Appleby, David, p101T;

NASA, p77;

NHPA/Laurie Campbell, p23, T Kitchin & V Hurst, p56C;

Tom Pfieffier/www.decadevolcano.net, p43;

Popperfoto.com, p29;

Gareth Price, p4, p8C, 16, p17, p18, p35, p45, p46, p52, p60T, p70L, p71, p73C, p85, p90, p94, p100, p102R, p109;

Ian Pritchard, p67;

Rex Features, p64L, p88, p89, A&M University, p19, Stills Press Agency, p30, Phil Ball, p49, Andrew Drysdale, p58, Nigel R Barklie, p62, 20thC. Fox/Everett, p83TL, Peter Brooker, p96B;

David Rydevik, p42;

Science Photo Library/Simon Fraser / RVI, Newcastle-upon-Tyne, p31, Science Source, p34L, P. Hawtin, University of Southampton, p34C, E Gueho, p34R, Philippe Plailly, p54, Martin Bond, p59, p60CB, p92R, Simon Fraser, p64R, David A. Hardy, Futures: 50 Years in Space, p80, Andrew Lambert Photography, p83C, Alfred Pasieka, p92L, Robert Brook, p95, David R. Frazier, p96T, James Stevenson, p102T, Scott Camazine, p106, Custom Medical Stock Photo, p107, Stevie Grand, p108;

Skyscan/Ian Pillinger, p91;

SHOUT, p55T;

Still Pictures/Ton Koene, p44, SOMBOON-UNEP, p56T, Mike Kolloffel, p56R;

Stockfile/Steve Behr, p48;

C&S Thompson, p24T, p101C;

Photo courtesy of West Midland Safari Park, Bewdley www.wmsp.co.uk, p5.

Biology

Chemistry

Physics

Contents

22.1 The Garden of Eden?

 How do plants make food?

It's a most unlikely tourist attraction – a giant greenhouse in Cornwall. Yet over a million people come every year to watch … plants growing! Of course, plants are important. They make food by **photosynthesis** and all animal life depends on them.

Animals that eat plants are called **herbivores**. In the giant domes of the Eden project there will be thousands of herbivores – the insects that eat the plants.

Animals that eat other animals are called **carnivores**. Some of the birds flying around the domes will be carnivores – eating the insects. Carnivores are sometimes called **predators** and the organisms they eat are their **prey**.

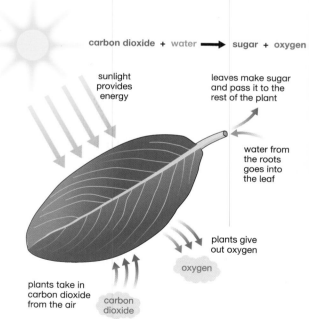

carbon dioxide + water ➡ sugar + oxygen

sunlight provides energy

leaves make sugar and pass it to the rest of the plant

water from the roots goes into the leaf

plants give out oxygen

oxygen

plants take in carbon dioxide from the air

carbon dioxide

Questions

1 List the things that photosynthesis needs to work.
2 Why do you think the Eden domes are transparent?
3 What is a herbivore?
4 Is a pet cat a herbivore or a carnivore?
5 How can you tell that plants are alive?

Keywords

photosynthesis
herbivores
carnivores
predators
prey

22.2 Safari park

How are animals adapted to survive?

White tigers are **extinct** in the wild and the tigers in the West Midlands Safari Park are the only ones in the UK. They are **predators** from India and will kill and eat a range of animals – including people! Predators like the tiger have **adaptations** that help them to capture and kill their **prey**. Of course, the prey have adaptations that help them not to be dinner!

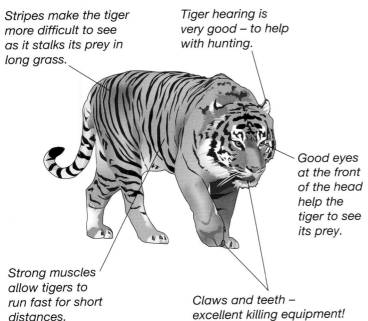

Stripes make the tiger more difficult to see as it stalks its prey in long grass.

Tiger hearing is very good – to help with hunting.

Good eyes at the front of the head help the tiger to see its prey.

Strong muscles allow tigers to run fast for short distances.

Claws and teeth – excellent killing equipment!

Eyes on each side of the head help the giraffe to see predators approaching from any direction.

The colours on the skin break up the outline of the giraffe, helping it to hide.

With its long neck the giraffe can reach high and see for miles.

Long legs make the giraffe a fast runner.

Giraffes are herbivores and the tiger sees them as lunch on legs! But the giraffe is adapted to avoid becoming tiger food.

Questions

1. What does the word 'extinct' mean?
2. List three adaptations of a tiger to its life as a predator.
3. List three adaptations of a giraffe that protect it from being eaten.
4. Why might giraffes with shorter than average necks get less food?
5. Dogs and cats are both carnivores. List three adaptations for each animal that help them to hunt.

Keywords

extinct

predators

adaptations

prey

22.3 Food webs

⇨ What is a food web?

'What do sharks eat when they can't get hold of me?'

Sharks are **carnivores** – they eat meat. But even the most ferocious shark depends on microscopic green plants. These plants are **producers**. They use energy from the sun, water and carbon dioxide to make food. The plants are eaten by **herbivores** which are then eaten by bigger animals which the shark will eat.

And what's true in the oceans off Australia is just as true in your local muddy pond. The green plants, the producers, make food for everything else to live on. A **food chain** shows what eats what, starting with the green plants. All the food chains in an area link up to make a **food web**.

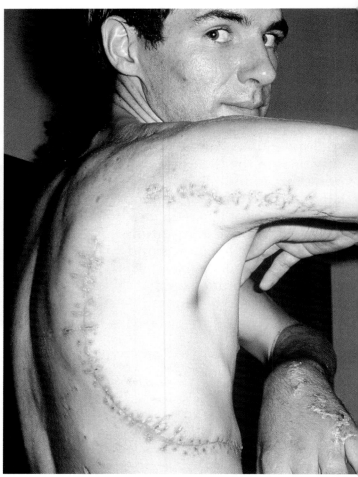

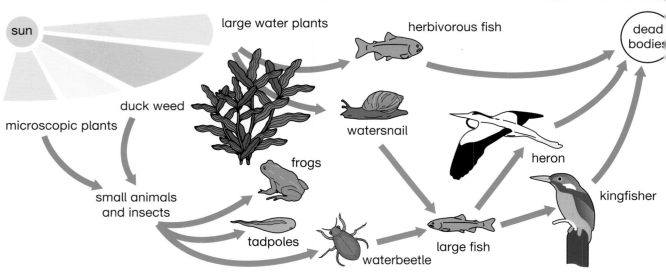

Questions

1 Write down one example of a food chain from the pond.

2 Put a box around the producer in your food chain.

3 Put a line under the herbivore in your food chain.

4 Put a star by the carnivore in your food chain.

5 Sharks attack swimmers. Should we try to kill all the sharks in the world? Give reasons for your answer.

Keywords

carnivores
producers
herbivores
food chain
food web

22.4 Science field trip

➡ **How can we study the environment?**

It's better than lessons on a Friday afternoon! Scientists often collect information about the plants and animals living in an area. Where something lives is its habitat. It is important not to damage the **habitat** when you study it.

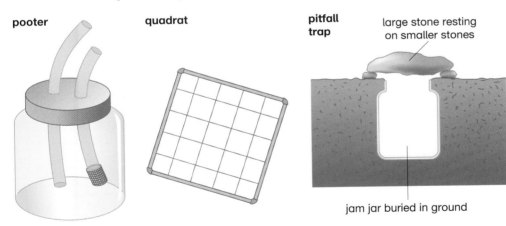

pooter   quadrat   pitfall trap   large stone resting on smaller stones

jam jar buried in ground

Questions

1 What does the word 'habitat' mean?

2 What could you use to find beetles living in the dead leaves under a tree?

3 Why is a pooter useless for catching field mice?

4 Why put a lid or stone on top of a pitfall trap?

5 A 1 m² quadrat contains five different types of plants. Why doesn't the whole habitat (1000 m²) contain 5000 different types?

Keywords

habitat

pooter

quadrat

pitfall trap

22 Data response: Green smudge

During the American Civil War black slaves in the southern states would try to escape to the North where slavery was banned. To find their way they looked at moss growing on tree trunks. They said it always grew better on the north side of the tree.

Pleurococcus is a green algae that grows on tree trunks. Some people have suggested that it grows better on the north side of trees. Look at the data below to see if this is true.

Distribution of Pleurococcus on trees in Hanley Wood

Tree	Northern side	Eastern side	Southern side	Western side
1	5	4	3	4
2	4	2	2	2
3	4	3	2	4
4	5	3	2	4
5	5	4	2	4
6	4	2	1	3
7	4	2	1	3
8	5	3	3	3
9	4	4	3	4
10	5	2	1	3

5 = lots of Pleurococcus
0 = no Pleurococcus at all

Data response

1. What is the highest score for the northern side of the tree?
2. What is the highest score for the southern side of the tree?
3. What is the lowest score for the eastern side of the tree?
4. Work out the average score for each side of the tree.
5. Draw a bar chart to show the average result for each side of the tree.
6. Does the data show that Pleurococcus grows better on the northern side of the tree trunk?
7. One researcher suggested Pleurococcus grows better on the northern side as this dries out less in the summer sun. How could you test this theory?

Creepy crawlies

8 Hedgerows supply food for animals and birds, shelter nearby plants and even provide homes for small mammals like voles and field mice. Use the internet to collect more data about the usefulness of hedgerows.

Some farmers have removed hedgerows to make it easier to use large machinery. Prepare a broadcast for your local radio station explaining why hedgerows should be protected.

Presentation

9 'Extinction is forever!' is the slogan for a campaign to protect endangered animals. Prepare a presentation to use in schools with pupils aged 11–14 to encourage them to join the campaign.

Revision checklist

I know:

- Plants make their own food from carbon dioxide in the air and water using energy from light. Animals get their food from eating plants or other animals.

- Some animals are adapted to avoid being caught as prey. They have good hearing and eyesight to detect predators at a distance. They often have stripes or mottled shapes on their skin. This breaks up their outline and makes it more difficult for the predators to see them.

- Some animals are adapted as successful predators by having very good eyesight, the ability to run fast and claws and teeth that can kill their prey.

- A herbivore is an animal that eats plants. A carnivore is an animal that eats other animals.

- Food webs show the feeding links between species in an area. A change to one species might affect the whole web.

- A habitat is the space where an organism lives. All organisms are adapted to survive in their particular habitat.

Fooling your senses

23.1 Eyes right

How do our eyes work?

Our eyes detect low levels of light and can tell us something about a scene many miles away. Each one of our eyes sees a slightly different view. The brain combines these images so we can see in 3-D. This is **stereoscopic** or **binocular** vision. If you close one eye you have **monocular** vision. The world is still clear but it is difficult to judge distances between objects.

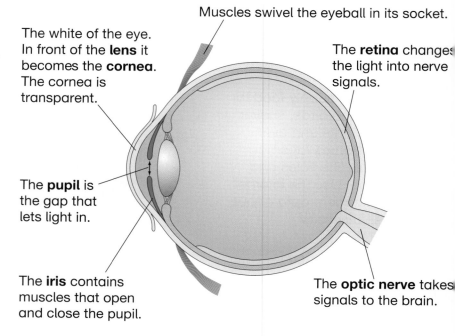

Muscles swivel the eyeball in its socket.

The white of the eye. In front of the **lens** it becomes the **cornea**. The cornea is transparent.

The **retina** changes the light into nerve signals.

The **pupil** is the gap that lets light in.

The **iris** contains muscles that open and close the pupil.

The **optic nerve** takes signals to the brain.

Animals that have eyes at the front of their heads have excellent binocular vision but a poor **field of view**. Animals with eyes on either side of their heads can see all around them but have poor distance judgement. Predators have eyes at the front; prey animals have eyes on either side of their heads.

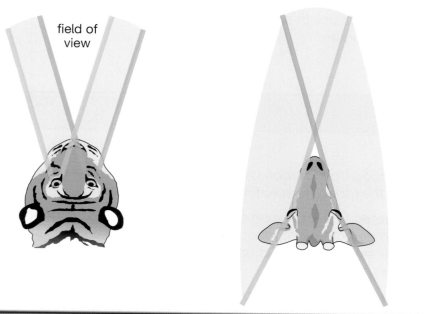

field of view

Questions

1 Which part of the eye lets in the light?
2 Which part of the eye converts the light to nerve signals?
3 How many eyes do you need for binocular vision?
4 Why do predators tend to have eyes at the front of their heads?
5 A fossil dinosaur has big eye sockets on opposite sides of the skull. What do you think this dinosaur would have eaten?

Keywords

lens
cornea
retina
pupil
iris
optic nerve
stereoscopic
binocular
monocular
field of view

23.2 Taste and smell

 How do we taste things?

The durian fruit shown here supposedly has the best **taste** and worst **smell** of any fruit. Experts say it's like eating your favourite ice cream while sitting on a smelly toilet!

Taste and smell are closely connected. If you have a cold you often cannot taste your food. This is because the sense cells in your nose cannot detect the chemicals through the mucus blocking your nose!

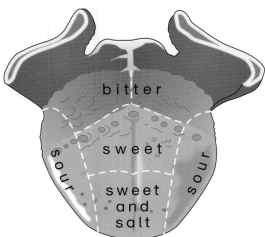

Your **tongue** has taste-sensitive nerves called **taste buds**. The taste buds for each taste are grouped together. Different parts of the tongue detect different tastes. You can only distinguish four tastes: sweet, sour, salt and bitter. When you 'taste' food, most of the **flavour** comes from the smell. If your nose is blocked food loses its taste.

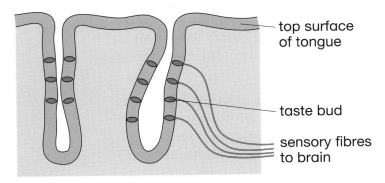

top surface of tongue

taste bud

sensory fibres to brain

Questions

1 What are taste buds?

2 Where are taste buds found?

3 List the four tastes that your tongue can detect.

4 Explain why food does not taste the same when you have a cold.

5 Plan an investigation into how well people can tell the flavour of different types of crisps if their nose is blocked. If possible, carry out your investigation.

Keywords

taste

smell

tongue

taste buds

flavour

23.3 Fast reactions

 What are reflexes?

Neo needs fast reaction times to win this fight! The **reaction time** is the time between a **stimulus** and your **response**. A stimulus is something you can detect, like a sound or sight. The response is what you do.

Eyes, ears and taste buds are called **receptors**. They detect the stimulus. Other parts of the body – called **effectors** – produce the response. Muscles are effectors. We often produce a movement response to a stimulus.

Reflexes are automatic reactions usually to do with protecting the body from damage. If we touch a hot object we will often pull our hands away before we even notice that we've been burnt.

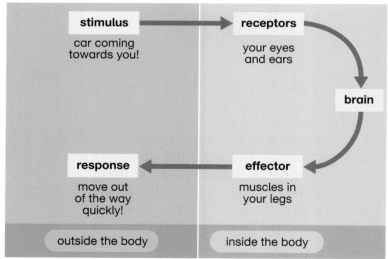

stimulus	receptors
car coming towards you!	your eyes and ears

brain

response	effector
move out of the way quickly!	muscles in your legs

outside the body | inside the body

Questions

1 What is a stimulus?
2 What are the effectors that produce movement responses?
3 What is the reaction time?
4 What do reflexes do?
5 Plan an investigation to measure reaction time.

Keywords

reaction time
stimulus
response
receptor
effector
reflex

Fooling your senses

23.4 Skin deep

⇨ **What can we feel though our skin?**

Too much time sunbathing can make your skin look orange! It's no way to treat your skin, which protects you from the outside world and contains millions of nerve cells.

Skin contains nerves that sense **touch**, **pressure**, **pain** and **temperature**. A strong **sensation** usually occurs when lots of **nerves** are stimulated. Some parts of your skin are more sensitive because there are more nerve endings. Your fingertips contain many more sense cells (per cm^2) than the back of your neck or forehead.

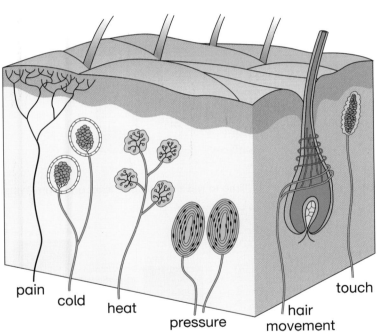

pain
cold
heat
pressure
hair movement
touch

Skin cannot detect actual temperature. It will only recognise a change of temperature. This is why warm water can feel cool if you are very hot.

Questions

1 Draw and label a diagram of the skin.

2 Name the four stimuli that nerves in the skin can detect.

3 Why do you think pressure sensors are deeper in the skin than touch and pain sensors?

4 Why is it an advantage that your fingertips have more sense cells than the back of your neck?

5 Your skin is much thinner on your forehead than on the bottoms of your feet. Why?

Keywords

touch

pressure

pain

sensation

nerves

temperature

23 Data response: Keeping safe

Every year in the UK hundreds of people die from road accidents caused by drivers who have had too much alcohol to drink. But how much is too much? When you try to drive home from the club.

The number of errors made by drivers in a 10 minute driving test, before and after drinking

Time of test	Test 1	Test 2
Before drinking	60	59
After drinking	Drank 1 pint	Drank 2 pints
30 minutes later	68	75
60 minutes later	58	63
90 minutes later	65	68

THINK!

DON'T DRINK

Don't Drink and Drive!

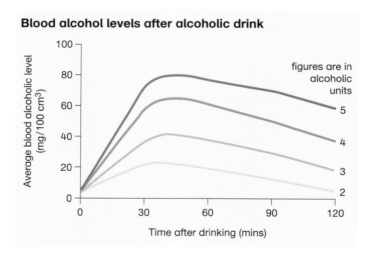

1 unit of alcohol = ▢ = ▢ = ▢

Blood alcohol levels after alcoholic drink

figures are in alcoholic units

Average blood alcoholic level (mg/100 cm³)

Time after drinking (mins)

5
4
3
2

Time to get through one level on Doom-type video game

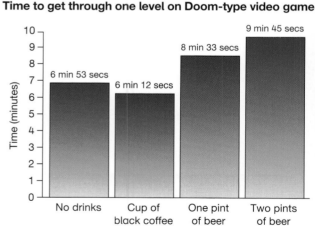

Time (minutes)

6 min 53 secs	No drinks
6 min 12 secs	Cup of black coffee
8 min 33 secs	One pint of beer
9 min 45 secs	Two pints of beer

Data response

1 How many pints of beer is the same as four units of alcohol?

2 How many alcohol units is two pints of beer and a single whisky?

3 A person drank two pints. How many errors did they make in a driving test 30 minutes later?

Fooling your senses

4 Give some evidence from the table to show that drinking two pints has more effect than drinking one.

5 How long after drinking is the level of alcohol in the blood highest?

6 Give two pieces of evidence from the tables and charts that show alcohol slows your reaction times.

Research

7 Use the ruler-dropping reaction time test to see who has the fastest reaction speeds. Can people improve their reaction times? Do the people who seem to have the fastest reaction times with the ruler also have the fastest reaction times when tested by a computer?

Presentation

8 'All this fuss about drinking and driving – I'm perfectly safe after two or three pints!' This seems a stupid comment but some people appear to believe it! Prepare a poster to show the difference between a driver who has had nothing to drink and someone who has drunk three pints. You can use data from these pages – make your poster hard-hitting and clear.

Revision checklist

I know:

- The cornea helps to focus light. The iris controls the amount of light going through the pupil. The lens focuses light on the retina which passes nerve impulses along the optic nerve to the brain.

- Humans have good binocular vision, but a limited field of view. All predators have good binocular vision and can judge distances well. They need two eyes with overlapping fields of view to have 3D vision. Prey animals have monocular vision with eyes on either side of the head. This gives them a very wide field of view.

- The nose is lined with nerves sensitive to chemicals in the air. Taste buds on the tongue are sensitive to four tastes: salt, sweet, sour, bitter. Different areas of the tongue are more sensitive to different tastes. The flavour of food depends on smell and taste. Foods have little flavour when our nose is blocked.

- Sensor or receptor cells detect stimuli like sounds, light, touch or temperature. Effector cells produce a response. Simple reflex actions often have sensors and effectors linked to protect the body.

- The skin contains sensory nerves for touch, temperature, pain and pressure. Pressure sensors are deeper in the skin than pain sensors. Some areas of skin contain more nerve endings than others.

24.1 Look at the veg on that!

What parts of a plant can we eat?

Roots, **fruits**, **stems** and **leaves** – this vegetable stall has all the parts of the plant! Plants provide animals with **nutrients** such as carbohydrates, fats, proteins, vitamins and minerals. Some plants just add flavour. For example, there is very little nutritional value in many spices – but a curry without spices would taste awful!

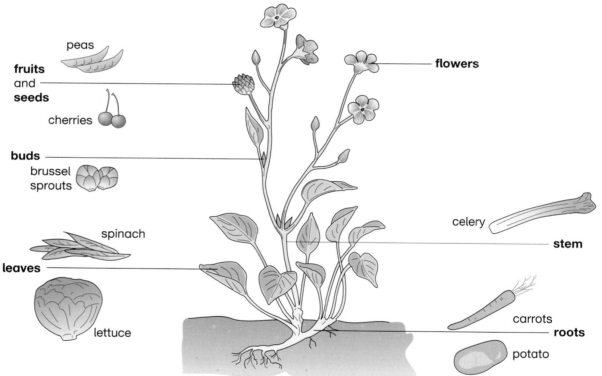

fruits and seeds — peas, cherries

flowers

buds — brussel sprouts

leaves — spinach, lettuce

stem — celery

roots — carrots, potato

Questions

1 Use the drawing above to list the parts of a plant.

2 Write a sentence to explain what the leaf does.

3 Write a sentence to explain what the root does.

4 Plan an investigation to see if small grapes are really sweeter than large grapes.

5 How can you tell that plants are alive?

Keywords

roots
fruits
stems
leaves
nutrients

Growing

Growing seeds

⮕ **What do seeds do?**

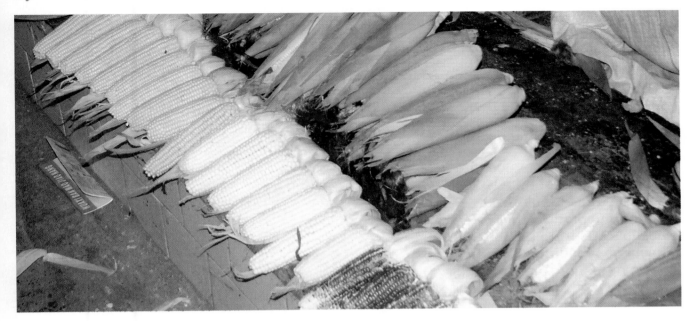

All of these are types of maize. The seeds are the bits that can grow into new plants. We eat the seeds because they contain stored energy to help the plant grow.

The seed soaks up water and swells.

All seeds have a food store to start the plant off. The seed grows roots to collect water. The shoot grows upwards.

New leaves make food using sunlight.

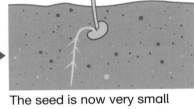

The seed is now very small because the original food store has been used up.

Seeds only grow into new plants if the conditions are right. They need **water**, **air** and **warmth**. Seeds remain **dormant** until they get what they need. All seeds have a food store to start the plant off. They must grow **roots** to collect water and **leaves** to make more food before the food store runs out. This early growth is called **germination**.

Questions

1 Why do plants make seeds?
2 What three things do seeds need to help them to germinate?
3 Which part of the seed grows first?
4 What is it used for?
5 Do seeds need light to germinate? Plan an investigation to find out.

Keywords

water

air

warmth

dormant

roots

leaves

germination

24.3 Spudwrestling!

What is selective breeding?

Mudwrestling is so last year! Tom is limbering up for the first Leicester spudwrestling challenge. Could it be the next Olympic sport? But which sort of potatoes would you need? Some make good chips, some good mash and others are best eaten lightly boiled.

Different types of potatoes are called **varieties** or **breeds**. Farmers choose particular plants or animals to produce the best possible **offspring**. This is called **selective breeding**. Cows are bred to produce more meat or milk; hens are bred to lay more eggs. Plants are often bred to produce more food, tastier food or disease-resistant crops.

What are different varieties of potato best for?

Variety	Baked	Chipped	Mashed	Roast	Disease resistance
Home guard	0	0	1	0	0
Desiree	1	1	1	1	1
Maris Piper	2	2	2	1	1
King Edward	2	2	2	2	0

2 = best, 0 = worst

Questions

1 List three varieties of potato.

2 What does 'selective breeding' mean?

3 Why do farmers use selective breeding for their crops and animals?

4 Which potato variety is best for making roast potatoes?

5 Give one advantage of Maris Piper compared with King Edward potatoes.

6 Plan an investigation to find out how the size of the potato affects how long it takes to cook.

Keywords

varieties

breeds

offspring

selective breeding

Growing

24.4 Clone my moggy!

▶ What is a clone?

OK, so your cat's ill. These men in America will take one of its cells and clone you a whole new cat! Only £20 000 if you're interested!

You can do some cloning of your own. Animals are very difficult to clone but many plants are quite easy. **Cuttings** from roses and African violets grow easily into complete new plants. Cuttings contain exactly the same **genes** as the original plants so are **clones**. Any differences between clones are due to the **environment**, not genes.

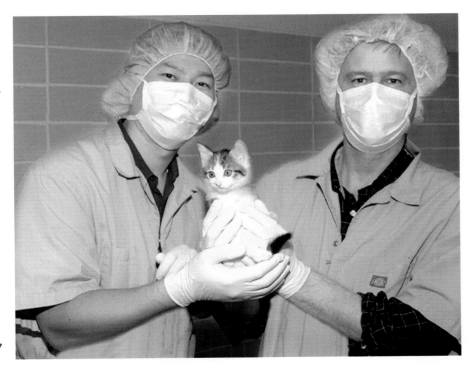

Clones are useful to farmers because they flower and fruit at exactly the same time. They can be cheaper and quicker to grow than seeds. Unfortunately, because clones are the same they all suffer from the same diseases. If one plant fails they all fail.

In 2006 it is illegal to clone human beings. Some scientists say there is no technical reason why we cannot clone people – but do we want to?

I suffer from an illness that has damaged cells in my bone. If I could be cloned I could get a transplant of cells from my clone to cure me. Why is that not allowed?

If we start cloning people for medical reasons where will it end? And who 'owns' a clone? Do they have rights? Do they belong to the person they were created from?

Questions

1 What does the word 'clone' mean?

2 Give two advantages of cloned plants.

3 Give one disadvantages of cloned plants.

4 What can still cause differences between clones?

5 Do you think human cloning should be allowed? List some arguments on both sides of the question.

Keywords

clones

cuttings

environment

genes

Barley is an essential part of beer. The barley seeds are germinated to produce tiny seedlings. The seedlings contain chemicals called enzymes which help to break down the stored starch in the barley. This is converted to sugar. Yeast then converts this to alcohol during fermentation.

Percentage of seeds that germinated in 48 hours at different temperatures

Temperature (°C)	Percentage germination
5	3
10	54
15	89
20	75
25	17

Seeds germinated in 48 hours in dark and light conditions

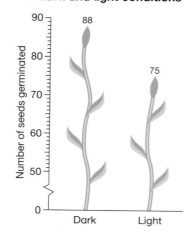

Number of seedlings germinated at 15°C

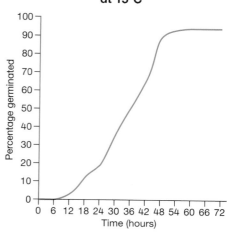

Data response

1 What percentage of the barley germinates at 10°C?

2 What is the best temperature for germinating barley?

3 Why does the rate of germination go down at 25°C?

4 Do barley seeds need light to germinate?

5 What percentage of barley seeds have germinated after 42 hours at 10°C?

6 By when had half of the barley seeds germinated?

7 Why do you think 6% of the barley seeds have not germinated even after 72 hours?

Research

8 Every year scientists get nearer to being able to clone human beings. But is this a good idea? Use magazines, newspapers and the internet to find different views about cloning humans. Make a list of the points for and against. Be careful – look out for bias in the articles you read!

Presentation

9 Work with a partner to prepare two speeches – one for human cloning and one against. Your speeches should last about five minutes. Be ready to present them to the class.

Revision checklist

I know:

- The positions and jobs of the main parts of a plant. We eat different parts of plants.

- Plants make seeds to produce the next generation. Seeds grow into adult plants when the conditions are right. Seeds need warmth, air and water for germination.

- Selective breeding can increase the size, yield and disease-resistance of plants and animals.

- Plants can regrow damaged parts, but most animals cannot. Cloning leads to identical offspring. Differences between clones are due to environmental factors.

- Cloned plants have advantages (all identical/quicker/cheaper) and disadvantages (prone to the same infections or diseases).

- Some people feel human cloning is wrong. Some feel it is OK if it saves a life. Others think human cloning is acceptable in any circumstances.

25.1 It's a cow's life

 Where does milk come from?

5:00 am
Cows brought in from the field to the milking parlour. They will be milked by machine and each cow will produce up to 9 litres of milk at each milking.

8:00 am
Cows return to the field in the summer. Many farmers also give cows extra food to increase the milk yield.

4:00 pm
Cows brought in from the field to the milking parlour for the second milking of the day.

The milk passes along clean sterile tubes and is tested for any diseases. It is collected in a giant tank and stored at about 3°C until the tanker arrives at the farm

A tanker arrives and takes the milk to a central processing plant. Here it is heat treated to kill any dangerous microorganisms. Then it is bottled and shipped to shops and dairies

Milk is tested to make sure it is safe and good to drink before it is bottled. Milk may be sterilised or pasteurised.

Sterilising heats the milk up to about 120°C for about 20 minutes. The milk is already sealed in the bottle when this happens. All **microorganisms** are killed.

Pasteurising heats the milk to just over 70°C for a few seconds and then cools it down again. This kills all the dangerous microorganisms. The milk is bottled after it has been pasteurised. Pasteurised milk tastes better than sterilised milk.

Milk must be tested because it is a very good liquid for growing dangerous microorganisms. Microbes that cause fever, tuberculosis, dysentery and salmonella can live and grow in milk. Some of these can kill!

Questions

1 What does the word 'pasteurise' mean?
2 Give two differences between pasteurising and sterilising.
3 Why is untreated milk dangerous?
4 How many litres of milk might a cow produce every day?
5 If a farmer gets 5p a litre for his milk and he has 100 cows how much money will he make every day?

Keywords

sterilise
microorganisms
pasteurise

 From field to plate

25.2 Fertile soils

What is the pH of good soil?

Different soils are good for different plants. Potatoes need lots of manure but beans can grow in quite poor soils. One very important thing for healthy plants is the **acidity** of the soil. Most plants prefer the soil to be **neutral** or very slightly acidic. If the acidity of the soil is wrong the plant cannot take minerals from the soil. The soil on moorlands is often very acidic. Heather is one of the few plants that grow well here.

Farmers need to know more than just whether a soil is acid. They need to know exactly how acid it is. Very acid soils are useless but slightly acid soils can grow some crops. They give the soil a score out of 14. This is called the **pH**. If the soil is too acidic the farmer can add **lime**. But, he must not add too much or he will make the soil too **alkaline**!

Universal Indicator colour	pH	Acidic or alkaline	Plants that will grow
Red	1	Very acidic	Nothing grows
	2		
Reddish orange	3	Medium acidic	Blueberries, heather
	4		
Yellowish orange	5	Slightly acidic	Peanuts, potatoes
	6		
Yellow	7	Neutral	Plums
Green	8	Slightly alkaline	Cabbages, gooseberries
	9		
Blue	10	Medium alkaline	Nothing grows
	11		
Violet	12	Very alkaline	Nothing grows
	13		
	14		

Questions

1 Is a pH of 9 acidic, alkaline or neutral?

2 What is the pH of neutral soil?

3 Some soil has a pH of 5. The farmer thinks the soil is too acidic. What could he add to the soil to make it neutral?

4 What could the farmer grow in his soil if the pH was 6?

5 What crops would not grow in this soil?

6 Plan an investigation to find out how much lime you would need to add to a soil with a pH of 5 to make it neutral.

Keywords

acidity

neutral

pH

lime

alkali

25.3 Manure and rhubarb

 How does manure help plants to grow?

It's smelly, sticky, comes out of the back end of horses and cows – and it's brilliant on rhubarb! Well, on rhubarb in the ground – custard works better on rhubarb in your dish!

Manure breaks down slowly in the ground to release minerals. Other materials in the manure also help to keep the soil healthy. If the farmer did not add manure to the field the important minerals would soon be used up by the plants and nothing would grow.

Organic farmers have two tricks to stop this happening:

- Add manure every season – this put minerals back into the soil
- Use a field for a different crop every year and some years let the field rest – this is called letting the field lie fallow

Other farmers use more modern methods. They add artificially-made **fertilizers** to the ground. These are produced as powders in chemical factories and give the soil a quick boost of minerals. Farmers who use these fertilisers do not usually let fields lie fallow.

Uses of minerals in plants

Mineral	Use in plant
Nitrogen	Improves growth of plant, particularly the leaves
Potassium	Improves growth of fruit and flowers
Phosphorus	Essential for good root growth

Questions

1 What does nitrogen do in plants?

2 Which mineral is important for healthy root growth?

3 How do organic farmers fertilise their soil?

4 What do the words 'lie fallow' mean?

5 Why do many organic farms that grow vegetables also keep cows even though ordinary farmers do not?

Keywords

manure

fertiliser

nitrogen

potassium

phosphorus

From field to plate

25.4 Bacteria

➡️ How can bacteria make food?

The Dutch cheese Edam has a red waxy coating to stop it drying out. You're not supposed to eat the covering – but it probably won't do you too much harm! It's important to keep cheese in good conditions or it will dry out or go mouldy. Even the **bacteria** in the milk that made the cheese in the first place might make it go off.

Making cheese

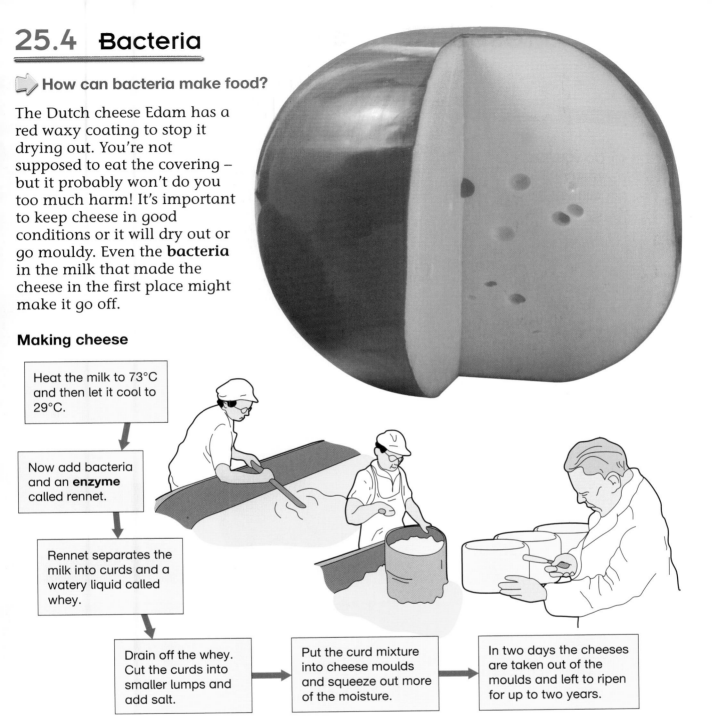

Heat the milk to 73°C and then let it cool to 29°C.

Now add bacteria and an **enzyme** called rennet.

Rennet separates the milk into curds and a watery liquid called whey.

Drain off the whey. Cut the curds into smaller lumps and add salt.

Put the curd mixture into cheese moulds and squeeze out more of the moisture.

In two days the cheeses are taken out of the moulds and left to ripen for up to two years.

Bacteria need moisture, warmth and a food supply to grow. If special bacteria called **lactic acid bacteria** are added to warm milk, they feed on the milk and turn it into **yoghurt**.

Questions

1 Why is the enzyme rennet added to the milk in the cheese-making process?
2 What is added to cheese before it is put into the moulds?
3 Name three things that bacteria need to grow.
4 Plan an investigation to see how the temperature affects how quickly milk turns sour.

Keywords

bacteria
enzyme
lactic acid bacteria
yoghurt

25 Data response: It's your choice!

1 Do you buy organic vegetables when they are available?

All the time	14
Sometimes	53
Never	32

2 If you buy organic vegetables which reason is most important to you?

They taste better	22
They are safer	35
Environmental reasons	7
Other	3

3 If you never buy organic vegetables which reason is most important to you?

They are too expensive	22
The quality is not as good	8
Other reason	2

Different brands of carrot soup were made up following the instructions from the manufacturers and served in paper cups without labels to people in Leicester market on Saturday 7th January 2006. The tasters then picked their favourite soup without knowing which one was which.

Soup	How many people picked this one as best?
Rooters Organic Carrot soup (fresh)	47
Meinz Carrot soup (in a tin)	22
ThirdEye Frozen Carrot soup (frozen)	32
Snore Instant Carrot Soup (powdered)	5

Data response

1 How many people sometimes bought organic vegetables when they were available?

2 What was the most important reason for these people choosing organic vegetables?

3 What was the most important reason for people not buying organic vegetables?

4 Draw a graph or chart to show the results of the carrot soup taste test.

5 Was the carrot soup taste test a fair test? Explain your answer.

6 Which was the most popular soup in the test?

7 Which was the least popular soup in the test?

8 A family changed to organic bread instead of Tess Coop's sliced loaf. If they ate three loaves of bread a week how much extra would it cost over a year?

Research

Design and carry out a taste test to compare organic and inorganic foods. Make sure your test is fair. Once you have done your test design a poster to show the results.

Presentation

Prepare a presentation to show the main steps in making yoghurt. You can use a digital camera to take pictures of the important stages and use these in your presentation. Record a commentary so that people can hear your instructions without having to read what's on the screen.

Revision checklist

I know

- Milk comes from cows (or sheep or goats) and is processed before it is. Pasteurising kills the dangerous microorganisms in milk. Sterilising kills all of the organisms in milk. Milk is tested to make sure it is safe from microorganisms that might cause dysentery, typhoid and other sorts of fevers.

- Hygiene is very important when making cheese and yoghurt to prevent dangerous microorganisms getting into the foods.

- Bacteria need warmth, moisture and a food supply to grow. Certain bacteria make cheese and yoghurt from milk.

- There are different types of soil and these affect the type of plants that grow. Some soils dry out easily and others get waterlogged. The pH of soil can be tested using universal indicator.

- Fertilisers supply the chemicals that plants need for growth. Fertilisers include nitrogen for improved overall growth, phosphorus for good root growth and potassium for flowers and fruit growth. Organic farmers use manure and crop rotation to improve soil fertility.

My genes

26.1 Where did you get that nose?

What are genes?

What makes us look the way we do? Deep in our cells are small things called **genes**. Genes are small lengths of a chemical called **DNA** found in the **nucleus** of our cells. Genes provide the instructions the body needs to make things. So, if you have brown eyes it is because you contain a gene that tells your body how to make brown eyes.

But do genes control everything? Not exactly. Our blood group is controlled entirely by genes. Our height is controlled by genes we inherit and by our environment. Bad food and illnesses can make us shorter than our genes would predict. These factors are affected by genes and the environment.

Playing the piano or being good at football or physics is controlled by our environment. Our genes probably have very little effect here. You cannot inherit the ability to play the guitar from your father – even if he is Eric Clapton!

Many genes work in groups. There may be 10 or 20 genes that affect your height. If even one of these change you will be different. Most of our features are controlled by packages of genes.

Which features can we inherit in our genes?

Inherited in genes	Both genes and environmental	Only environmental
Blood group	Height	Scars
Tongue rolling	Weight	Accent
Fixed or free earlobes	Skin colour	Ability to play a musical instrument

Questions

1 What is a gene?
2 Where can you find genes?
3 Can you inherit the ability to speak French from your mother?
4 List three things controlled entirely by the genes you inherit.
5 How might your environment affect your adult weight?

Keywords

genes
DNA
nucleus

26.2 Chromosomes

What are chromosomes?

In 1936 a woman called Dora Ratjen came fourth in the women's high jump in the Olympic Games in Berlin. Actually, it was really Hermann Ratjen who pretended to be a woman! He hoped to win a medal to impress the Nazi politicians who were running the country at the time!

One foolproof way to tell if someone is male or female is to look at their chromosomes. If you look under a powerful microscope at the **nucleus** of a cell you can see a collection of thin worm-like structures called **chromosomes**. Chromosomes are long strings of hundreds of thousands of genes stuck together.

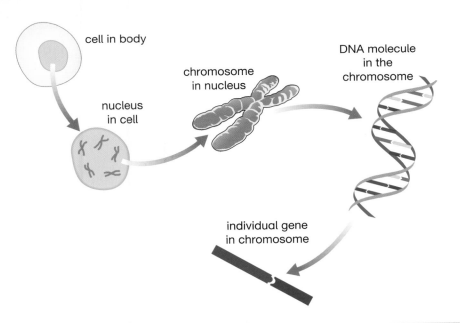

cell in body

nucleus in cell

chromosome in nucleus

DNA molecule in the chromosome

individual gene in chromosome

Human beings have 46 chromosomes. 44 of these are arranged in perfect pairs. The last pair are the sex chromosomes. There are two types of sex chromosomes, one called the X chromosome and a slightly shorter one called the Y chromosome. Women have two X chromosomes while men have one X and one Y chromosome.

Questions

1 What is a chromosome?
2 Rank these structures by size, start with the smallest.
    chromosome   gene   cell   nucleus
3 How many chromosomes do humans have?
4 How can you tell the difference between a Y chromosome and an X chromosome with a powerful microscope?
5 'Women have one chromosome fewer than men'. True or false?

Keywords

nucleus
chromosomes

26.3 Old Blue Eyes?

 How do genes control our eye colour?

Frank Sinatra was a famous singer who had deep blue eyes – and so did his dad. If your dad has blue eyes does it mean you will too? What if your parents have brown eyes? Will yours have to be brown?

It is possible to predict your eye colour using a diagram called a **Punnett square**. Just follow the rules:

1   You always start with two genes.

2   One **gene** controls what the person looks like. This is the **dominant** gene.

3   One gene from each parent passes to the child.

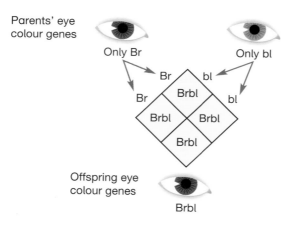

The children will all have brown eyes – because brown is dominant to blue.

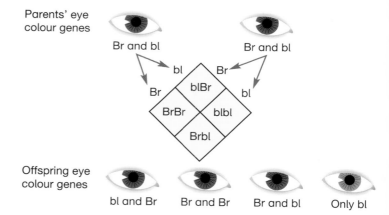

Here three quarters of the children will have brown eyes – but one in four will have blue.

Questions

1   What is special about a dominant gene?

2   Draw a Punnett Square diagram to cross BrBr brown eyes with Brbl brown eyes.

3   Can brown-eyed parents produce a blue-eyed child?

4   Two brown eyed parents have ten children and all of them have brown eyes. What does this tell you about the parents' genes?

5   Blue-eyed parents cannot produce brown-eyed children. Why?

Keywords

Punnett square

gene

dominant

26.4 Medical genetics

How do genes cause diseases?

Some illnesses are caused by damaged genes. **Cystic fibrosis** is a disease caused by a mistake in just one gene. People with cystic fibrosis suffer from lots of lung **infections** and find it difficult to digest their food.

Genetic engineers can insert genes into cells. This allows them to control how the cell develops. Genetic engineers know which gene causes cystic fibrosis. They are trying to insert a fresh, healthy gene into cells in the lungs and cure the disease. They hope to find a way to do this within ten years.

This is a good thing? Yes… but the same technology that cures cystic fibrosis might be used to change the colour of your eyes. Perhaps in the future parents will choose eye colour, hair colour and many other things about their children. Do we want this to happen? People disagree about whether it is good or bad.

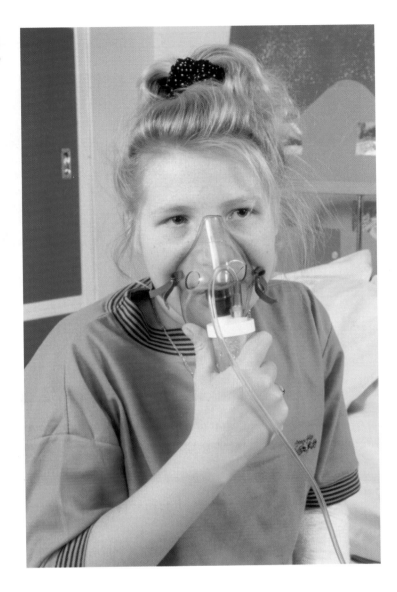

It starts with disease but it soon gets out of control. Some people will be able to choose exactly what their children will be like using genetic technology and others will be left behind because they are too poor.

These genetic engineers can help to cure some very nasty diseases. It would be wrong not to let them!

Questions

1 What is cystic fibrosis?
2 How are genetic engineers trying to cure cystic fibrosis?
3 Give one advantage of genetic engineering.
4 Why are some people nervous about genetic engineering?

Keywords

cystic fibrosis

infections

genetic engineers

Average weight and height of male teenagers in three countries

Age	USA Height (cm)	USA Weight (kg)	UK Height (cm)	UK Weight (kg)	China Height (cm)	China Weight (kg)
10	139	32	135	30	128	27
11	144	36	140	34	132	30
12	149	41	145	39	136	34
13	156	46	151	44	141	38
14	164	51	159	48	146	41
15	170	56	165	52	150	45
16	174	61	168	56	153	49
17	175	65	170	59	156	53
18	176	67	171	61	158	56
19	177	69	171	63	159	58
20	177	71	172	65	160	60

Average weight and height of adults in USA since 1960

Average weight

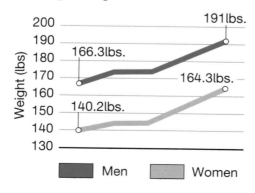

Average height

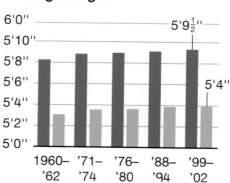

My genes

Data response

1 What is the average weight of a 16-year-old American?
2 What is the average height of a 12-year-old boy in China?
3 Which country tends to have the largest teenagers?
4 How much taller is a 18-year-old compared with a 14-year-old in China?
5 How much heavier is an American 16-year-old compared with a British teenager of the same age?
6 How much heavier is the average American adult in 2002 compared with 1960?
7 Is this change likely to be due to the genes or the environment? Give reasons for your answer.

Research

'People with big feet are taller.' Is this true? Plan an investigation to find out. If you can, carry out your investigation and display your results using a chart or graph.

Presentation

Prepare a presentation to show the arguments for and against testing babies for genetic defects while they are still in the womb. You must give arguments on both sides even if you agree with one view.

Revision checklist

I know

- All human cells contain a nucleus and each nucleus contains chromosomes. Chromosomes are long lengths of genes. These genes carry the information that makes us unique saved as a special genetic code.

- Most human features are determined by a person's genes. The environment also affects many features, e.g. skin colour, body weight. Most features are controlled by several genes working together, e.g. height.

- Some human features are entirely controlled by our genes (e.g. tongue rolling, size of ear lobes). Some are entirely controlled by the environment (e.g. scars, accent). Many are influenced by both (e.g. hair colour, good at sport).

- Normal body cells have 46 chromosomes: females have 23 pairs (including XX) but males have 22 pairs and **one** odd pair (XY).

- Some genes are dominant and some are recessive. A simple punnett square diagram can be used to work out genotype ratios.

- A few diseases are caused by faulty genes, for example cystic fibrosis and haemophilia. Embryos can be tested for many of these genes. People have many different viewpoints about testing for genetic diseases.

27.1 Bug wars!

 What are the different types of microorganism?

Your body is under attack all of the time. The posters show some of the main villains! Most microorganisms are harmless but the dangerous ones get the others a bad name!

Body wars

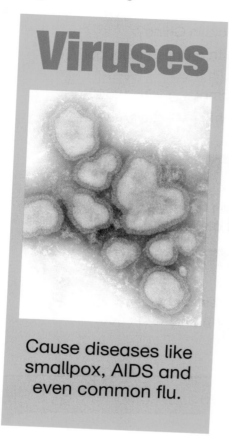

Viruses

Cause diseases like smallpox, AIDS and even common flu.

Bacteria

Important in breakdown of waste materials

Used in dairy industry to make yoghurt and cheese

Cause diseases from sore throats through to some that kill in 24 hours!

Fungi

Include mushrooms that are big enough to see and tiny fungi that look like the dust on some types of grape. Some are too small to see without a microscope.

Microorganisms grow at an incredible rate. In the best conditions they double every 20 minutes! If you start with one cell now you will have two in twenty minutes, eight in one hour and 2,360,000,000,000,000,000,000 a day later!

Unfortunately, our bodies provide good conditions for microbes to reproduce. Microbes like warm, wet conditions with a good supply of food. Luckily, **white blood cells** can engulf microbes to protect the body.

Questions

1 What are the three main types of microorganism?

2 List two diseases caused by viruses.

3 List two uses of fungi.

4 How often can microbes divide in good conditions?

5 How do white blood cells reduce the number of microorganisms in our body?

Keywords

viruses
bacteria
fungi
microorganisms
white blood cells

27.2 Avoiding infection

How can we avoid infection?

Toilet →

It's the highest toilet in the world! A neat hole in the floor which allows the stuff to drop through to the bottom of the cliff. Very **hygienic** – but a bit cold in the Tibetan winter!

Other ways to avoid **infection**:

- Always wash your hands after using the toilet.
- Keep raw meat and cooked meat separate – that way no microbes from the raw meat can get into the cooked meat.
- Keep salad covered in the fridge – it stops dangerous organisms falling into it.
- Make sure all foods are heated through when they cook. This kills any dangerous microorganisms deep inside the food.
- Clean knives and chopping boards very carefully after use. Even very small bits of meat or blood could carry dangerous microbes.

Questions

1 List three ways to make infection less likely.
2 Why should you keep raw meat and cooked meat separate?
3 Santa cooked a frozen turkey for Mrs Christmas. But, he did not leave it in the oven long enough to heat right through. Why is this dangerous?
4 Why should you wash your hands before starting any cooking?

Keywords

hygienic

infection

27.3 Fighting back

How does the body fight disease?

Your body protects itself against invading microbes in many ways.

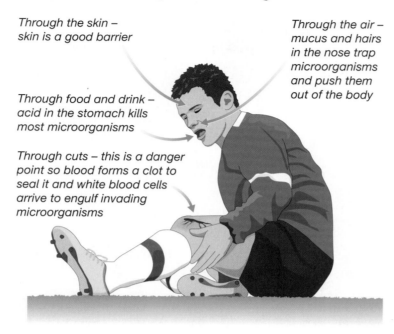

Through the skin – skin is a good barrier

Through the air – mucus and hairs in the nose trap microorganisms and push them out of the body

Through food and drink – acid in the stomach kills most microorganisms

Through cuts – this is a danger point so blood forms a clot to seal it and white blood cells arrive to engulf invading microorganisms

Once a dangerous microbe gets into your body you have to fight back. The body uses the **immune system** to fight back against invading organisms. The immune system produces:

- **Antibodies** that destroy invading microbes
- **White blood cells** that swallow the invaders whole!

Doctors can help the body with chemicals called **antibiotics**. Antibiotics are made by microorganisms that can kill fungi and bacteria. The most famous is probably penicillin which comes from a blue mould that grows on oranges!

Recently some dangerous bacteria have started to fight back by developing resistance to antibiotics. These are called **superbugs**. We can prevent superbugs developing by:

- Only using antibiotics when we really need them
- Always finishing the treatment – even if we feel better before all of the tablets are used

Questions

1 List three ways the body stops microbes getting into the body.
2 Which system fights microbes that have got into the body?
3 What is a superbug?
4 How can you reduce the chances of superbugs developing?
5 Bird Flu is caused by a virus. Why is it a waste of time to take an antibiotic if you have Bird Flu?

Keywords

immune system
antibodies
white blood cells
antibiotics
superbugs

27.4 Vaccinations

What vaccinations do you need?

World travel is great – but make sure you've had all of your **vaccinations** before you go. Vaccinations protect you – even *before* you get the disease. We get vaccinations against common childhood diseases like measles and mumps in the UK. If you want to travel to countries like Thailand or Borneo you will need vaccinations against the diseases that are common there.

Recommended vaccinations

	India	China	Congo	Bahamas
Typhoid	R	R	R	(R)
Hepatitis A	R	R	R	R
Diphtheria	R	R	R	(R)
Yellow Fever	(R)	(R)	C	R
Tuberculosis	N	R	N	(R)

R: usually recommended
(R): recommended if staying for 4 weeks
C: compulsory – you cannot get in without a vaccination certificate
N: not needed

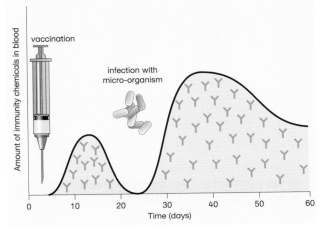

How the body produces chemicals to fight microorganisms

Vaccinations are powerful medicines that have saved millions of lives. However, there are some **risks**. Some people react to vaccinations and become very ill. In the UK there are some people who think their children were damaged by a vaccine called **MMR**. It is not always easy for parents to decide what to do. To make things worse some of the newspaper and media reports about the topic can be inaccurate or biased. How can people know what to do if they do not understand the science?

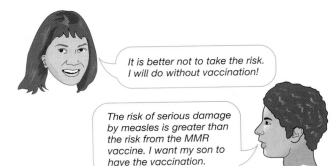

It is better not to take the risk. I will do without vaccination!

The risk of serious damage by measles is greater than the risk from the MMR vaccine. I want my son to have the vaccination.

Questions

1 What does the word vaccination mean?

2 Do you need a tuberculosis vaccination to go to India?

3 What vaccinations do you need to go to China for 2 weeks?

4 Why do some people not have vaccinations against childhood illnesses like measles?

5 Some countries do not let you enter if you do not have a proper vaccination. Is this fair? Or should they not interfere if you want to take the risk?

Keywords

vaccinations

risk

MMR

27 Data response: Comparing bacterial growth

Every year drug companies test thousands of chemicals to see if they can kill microbes. The chemicals are added to small wells in agar plates with microbes already growing. If the chemical kills the microbe a space develops around the well. The larger this space the better the chemical is at killing microbes.

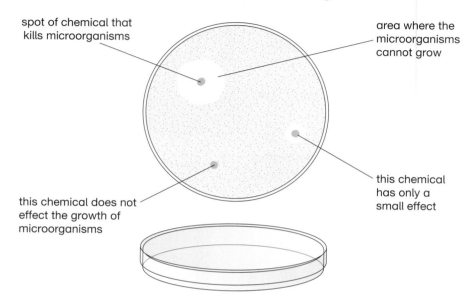

spot of chemical that kills microorganisms

area where the microorganisms cannot grow

this chemical has only a small effect

this chemical does not effect the growth of microorganisms

The table shows the results for four chemicals labelled A to D.

Results of five tests on a range of chemicals

Test	1	2	3	4	5
Chemical A	4	3	4	4	5
Chemical B	0	0	0	0	0
Chemical C	2	2	2	1	2
Chemical D	3	3	3	4	3
No added chemical	0	0	0	0	0

5 = microbe completely killed throughout plate
3 = microbe cleared from half of plate
0 = no effect on microbe growth

Data response

1 Which chemical in the tests is best at killing microbes?

2 One of the chemicals added was pure water. Which one do you think this is? Why?

3 Why did the researcher need to run one set of tests without any added chemicals?

4 Prepare a table like the one above and add scores for the plates shown above. Use the same scoring.

5 Sort all of the chemicals into an order starting with the one that kills the microbes best.

6 Why are the results for a particular chemical different across the five tests?

Research

Cooking destroys microbes that may have got into raw food. Plan an investigation to see how hot you have to make milk to kill all of the bacteria in it. If you can, carry out an investigation.

The number of parents having their children vaccinated against mumps, measles ad rubella has dropped over the last few years. This is because of a scare that the vaccine can cause damage. Doctors are frightened that there will be an outbreak of measles soon which will kill some children. Should parents be forced to have their children vaccinated? Prepare a presentation giving the arguments on both sides of this difficult problem.

Revision checklist

I know

- Microbes include bacteria, fungi and viruses. Our bodies provide good conditions for microbes to reproduce rapidly. A few types of microbes can make people ill.

- The skin, chemicals in tears, sweat, and stomach acid stop microbes getting in. Microbes can enter the body through natural openings, or cuts in the skin.

- The immune system fights microbes that get into the body. White blood cells swallow microbes and kill them.

- To reduce the risk of infection:
  - Always wash your hands after using the toilet.
  - Keep raw meat and cooked meat separate – so microbes from the raw meat cannot get into the cooked meat.
  - Keep salad covered in the fridge – it stops dangerous organisms falling into it.
  - Make sure all foods are heated through when they cook. This kills any microorganisms deep inside the food.
  - Clean knives and chopping boards very carefully after use. Even very small bits of meat or blood could carry dangerous microbes.

- Antibiotics are chemicals that kill bacteria and fungi, but not viruses. Some bacteria have developed which are not killed by some antibiotics. These bacteria are called 'superbugs'. To reduce the risk of 'superbugs' developing:
  - only use antibiotics when needed
  - always finish a course of antibiotics

- Vaccines can make people immune to a disease. Once you are immune you are protected from a particular disease.

- Vaccines are very safe medicines but some people may react badly to them. Some parents do not want their children to have a vaccine because they do not want to take a chance however small it is. Other people want the vaccines because they think the risk is very small and the disease is more dangerous than the vaccine.

- Media reports on health studies can sometimes be exaggerated. This makes it difficult to decide what to do without the original data.

28.1 Solid ground?

  What is the earth made from?

The ground we walk on is solid – but only for a few miles down! The Earth is made of a thin **crust** of solid **rock** floating over the surface of a giant bubble of molten rock. We can see this molten rock when it comes out of volcanoes as lava.

The crust is made of solid pieces called **tectonic plates**. These plates move a few centimetres each year. If they move towards each other one plate slides under the other.

Alfred Wegener was the first man to suggest this idea. He pointed out that the coastlines of South America and Africa seemed to fit together like jigsaw pieces. Perhaps they were once joined and had drifted apart? Most geologists rejected Wegener's ideas. The president of the American Philosophical Society called them "utter, damned rot!"

However, as time went on and more evidence appeared it was Wegener's ideas that survived. Now all serious scientists accept his theory of **continental drift**. The diagram shows where the plates join.

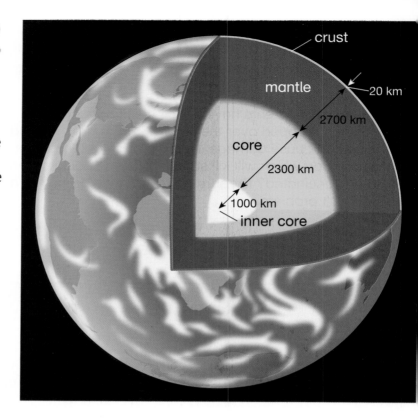

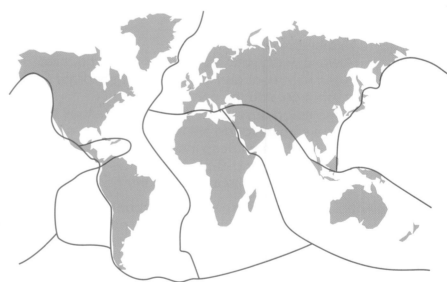

Restless earth

Questions

1 What is the Earth's crust?
2 How wide is the mantle?
3 Who first put forward the idea of continental drift?
4 What do geologists do?
5 London and New York are drifting apart at about 1 cm per year. How far will they have moved by 2106?

Keywords

crust
rock
mantle
core
tectonic plates
continental drift

28.2 Earthquakes

 How do earthquakes cause damage?

On the 8th of October 2005 a giant **earthquake** hit Kashmir. It reduced buildings to rubble and killed more than 80,000 people instantly. 100,000 more were injured or made homeless.

Many of the roads to remote villages were swept away by **landslides** caused by the earthquake. The people in these villages needed food and water, medical supplies to prevent outbreak of diseases and buildings or tents to protect against the soon-to-arrive cold Himalayan winter.

Earthquakes happen when layers of rock move past each other and shake the Earth's surface. Earthquakes can be very powerful and send **shock waves** for many miles in every direction. We cannot predict exactly when earthquakes will happen. We can build earthquake-proof buildings in areas where quakes are common. We should also have stores of medical equipment and food ready to help earthquake victims.

Questions

1 When did the Kashmir earthquake happen?
2 How many people were killed on the first day of the Kashmir earthquake?
3 List three problems created by the earthquake.
4 List three ways to reduce casualties of the earthquake.
5 Why were aid agencies so worried about the time of year when the Kashmir earthquake occurred?

Keywords

earthquake
landslides
shock waves

28.3 A wall of water

What is a tsunami?

A **tsunami** is a **tidal wave** created by an underwater **earthquake** or volcanic explosion. In December 2004 a huge earthquake in the Indian Ocean created a tsunami that struck thousands of miles of coastline. Waves as high as 30 metres killed up to 250,000 people instantly.

The force of the water knocked down buildings and carried the **debris** inland. Cars, boats, even lorries were swept for miles. The water flooded food stores, destroying food. The salt in the water even reduced the land's fertility so that growing new crops became more difficult.

Since tsunamis travel across the surface of the sea it should be possible to predict where they will hit. People can then move to higher ground or higher floors in taller, stronger buildings. Scientists can also detect the earthquakes and volcanoes that produce tsunamis to give some warnings.

Questions

1 What does the word 'tsunami' mean?

2 What causes a tsunami?

3 List three problems caused by a tsunami.

4 Suggest three things we can do to reduce the damage done by a tsunami.

5 Why is it more difficult to grow crops in land that has been flooded by seawater?

Keywords

tsunami

tidal wave

earthquake

debris

28.4 Volcanoes

Where do rocks come from?

The inside of the earth is so hot that rocks melt. A **volcano** is a place on the surface of the Earth where **molten** rock comes out. Volcanoes may lie dormant for many years, but then suddenly **erupt**. Dust, smoke and large lumps of solid rock also erupt from volcanoes.

Rocks that come from volcanoes are called **igneous** rocks. They have crystals in them. If they cooled slowly they have large crystals – easy to see with the naked eye. If they cooled quickly they have very small crystals.

Some liquid rock never reaches the surface. It is called **magma**. It cools slowly and forms rock called **granite** that has large crystals. Granite is often used for building.

The liquid rock flowing along the surface is called **lava**. It cools quite quickly into a dark rock that contains small crystals.

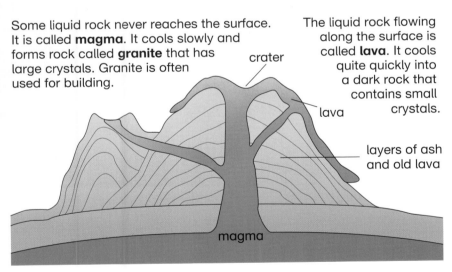

crater

lava

layers of ash and old lava

magma

Questions

1 What is an igneous rock?
2 Why do some igneous rocks have large crystals in them?
3 What is the difference between magma and lava?
4 Give an example of an igneous rock.
5 An igneous rock has very small crystals in it. What does this tell you about how quickly it cooled?

Keywords

volcano
molten
erupt
igneous
magma
granite
lava

28 Data response: Natural disasters

The positions of all the earthquakes of 2005

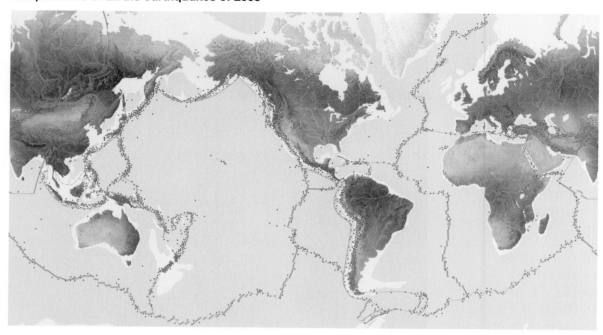

Number of people killed or affected by earthquakes

Country	Date	Killed
Pakistan	8 Oct 2005	73,320
China	27 Jul 1976	242,000
Peru	31 May 1970	66,794
Soviet Union	5 Oct 1948	110,000
Pakistan	31 May 1935	60,000
China	26 Dec 1932	70,000
China	22 May 1927	200,000
Japan	1 Sep 1923	143,000
China	16 Dec 1920	180,000
Italy	28 Dec 1908	75,000

Source: "EM-DAT: The OFDA/CRED International Disaster Database, ©Université catholique de Louvain, Brussels, Belgium"

Data response

1 Which earthquake killed the most people up to the year 2005?

2 Where did the earthquake that happened in 1923 happen?

3 How many lives were lost in the earthquake that hit Italy in 1908?

4 Why are the numbers of people killed in the table probably an under-estimate?

5 Sort the data in the table to list the earthquakes from most people killed to least people killed. Now draw a barchart to illustrate your sorted data.

6 The map of the world shows the positions of the major earthquakes in 2005. Compare this with the map of the tectonic plates on page 40. What similarities can you see?

7 Salol is a chemical that melts easily in a hot water bath. It forms crystals again when it cools back to room temperature. Plan an investigation to look at how the speed of cooling affects the size of the crystals that form. You can use some or all of the following equipment: molten salol, microscope slides cooled in a freezer, microscope slides warmed in an oven, microscope slides at normal room temperature.

Presentation

8 Imagine what would happen if an earthquake hit Hong Kong. Prepare a news report about the effects of this quake on the island and people. You can use images of Hong Kong from the internet. If you have access to a digital camera you could even record your own report!

Revision checklist

I know

- Movement of the Earth's crust causes earthquakes, volcanoes, and tsunamis. These natural disasters kill people and damage houses, water and food supplies. This kills more people over the next few months from diseases, exposure to cold and starvation.

- Public authorities can reduce damage caused by natural disasters by building earthquake-proof buildings, not building in danger zones if possible, keeping emergency stores of food and medicines and offering early warnings of disasters when possible.

- The Earth is a sphere with a molten core, mantle and thin rocky crust. The rocky crust is split into sections called tectonic plates. Tectonic plates move very slowly across the surface of the Earth.

- The evidence for plate tectonic theory includes the jigsaw fit of continents, areas of rocks stretching across continents and matching fossils in different continents. The idea of moving continents was not immediately accepted by scientists when Wegener suggested it. Later a lot of evidence showed that Wegener had been right after all.

- Large amounts of energy are released in an earthquake. It is not possible to predict exactly when earthquakes will happen or volcanoes will erupt.

- Molten rock under the surface of the Earth is called magma. Molten rock coming out of volcanoes is called lava. Igneous rocks form when molten rock cools down. Igneous rocks which have formed slowly have large crystals in them. Igneous rocks that have cooled quickly have small crystals.

29.1 Reactions

What is a chemical reaction?

A garden fire – you can see the heat coming off the flames! Scientists call this reaction **combustion**.

Over thousands of years chemical reactions help to build these rock formations.

All of these photographs show **chemical reactions** – some fast and some slow. A reaction usually keeps going until one of the chemicals it needs is used up. So, when no more wood is left a fire will go out.

In fifty to sixty years these mushrooms will help to dissolve away the fallen tree.

These thick wooden logs are slowly being eaten away by seawater. The metal bolts holding them in place are also rusting away.

The mould on this peach is slowly dissolving away the fruit. We can speed up this reaction by warming the fruit.

A rhubarb and raspberry muffin – made by a series of complicated reactions in the cooker.

Questions

1. What is the chemical name for the reaction we call burning?
2. What stops the bonfire burning in the end?
3. Sort the reactions on this page from fastest to slowest.
4. List some very fast chemical reactions.
5. List some very slow chemical reactions.
6. How could you make a bonfire burn more brightly?

Keywords

combustion

chemical reaction

29.2 Alien blood!

How quickly can acid dissolve metal?

In the *Alien* films the monster has acid for blood. This makes it very difficult to kill because any damage to it will release acid which will eat its way through the metal hull of the spaceship.

Everyone knows that acids are very dangerous. However, acids are not always very good at dissolving metal. The **reaction** between the acid and the metal can be quite slow. One way to speed up this reaction is to warm the acid.

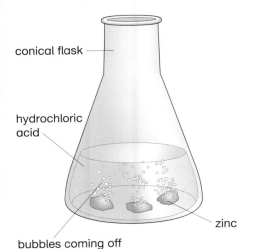

conical flask

hydrochloric acid

zinc

bubbles coming off grey lumps of zinc

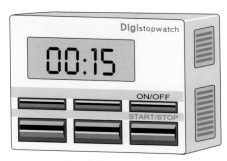

digital stopwatch

Steven did a series of experiments with **zinc** metal and dilute **hydrochloric acid**. These are his results.

Time taken for 10 g of zinc to dissolve
(All times in seconds)

Concentration of acid	Large lumps	Fine powder
dilute	20	12
concentrated	13	5

Questions

1 Which conditions dissolve the metal quickest?

2 What is the longest time taken in the results to dissolve 10 g of metal?

3 How does using powder instead of lumps affect the speed of the reaction?

4 List three ways to speed up the reaction between the acid and the metal.

5 What do you think would happen if the acid was warmed?

29.3 Board with chemistry?

 How does a catalyst affect the speed of a reaction?

Skateboards, snowboards and surf boards – all made from plastic resin. The resin is moulded roughly to shape and then sanded to perfection.

The skateboard is made of two chemicals. One is a **resin**. The other is a hardener which contains a **catalyst**. The resin goes solid without the hardener but it is a very, very slow reaction. The catalyst speeds up the setting reaction. Other catalysts can speed up other reactions. Changing the **temperature** can affect the rate of the reaction as well.

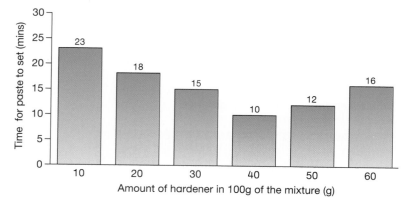

Time for resin to set with different amounts of hardener

Bar chart — Time for paste to set (mins) vs Amount of hardener in 100g of the mixture (g):
- 10 g: 23
- 20 g: 18
- 30 g: 15
- 40 g: 10
- 50 g: 12
- 60 g: 16

Temperature and reaction time

Temperature (°C)	Time for resin to set (mins)
10	30
20	12
30	10
40	6
50	2

Questions

1 How long does it take to set with 30 g of hardener in the mixture?

2 What is the best temperature for this reaction?

3 Would anything happen to the resin if it was left for ten minutes without mixing with the hardener?

4 It says on the pack that you should not mix more than you can use in ten minutes. Why?

5 Why might surfboard makers find it difficult to make surfboards at the best temperature for a very fast reaction time?

Keywords

resin

catalyst

temperature

29.4 Grinding down

 How does surface area affect the speed of a reaction?

Fireworks are just simple **combustion** reactions – but they do it at very high speed! How can we make sure that fireworks are exciting and safe?

Charcoal burns well but quite slowly. If you grind up the charcoal to make a fine powder it burns more quickly. A very fine powder burns so quickly it practically explodes! Firework designers carefully mix powders to produce something that burns at just the right speed. Too fast and the firework explodes. Too slow and it goes out or just smoulders.

How can we explain this difference?

The reaction between the chemicals only happens where they touch. This is at the **surface area** *of the* **particles** *– the areas marked in red.*

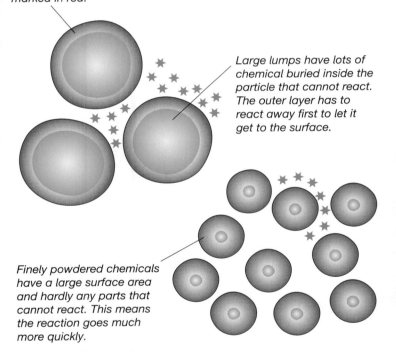

Large lumps have lots of chemical buried inside the particle that cannot react. The outer layer has to react away first to let it get to the surface.

Finely powdered chemicals have a large surface area and hardly any parts that cannot react. This means the reaction goes much more quickly.

Questions

1 What is the main reaction in a firework?

2 Why do fireworks use powdered chemicals?

3 What might happen if the powders in the chemical were too finely ground?

4 What might happen if the firework powders were not ground finely enough?

5 Why should you never go back to a firework that has not worked even if it seems to have gone out?

Keywords

combustion
charcoal
surface area
particle

29 Data response: What a pain!

You know what it's like – a sharp pain just behind your forehead!
You need something to help the pain – and fast!

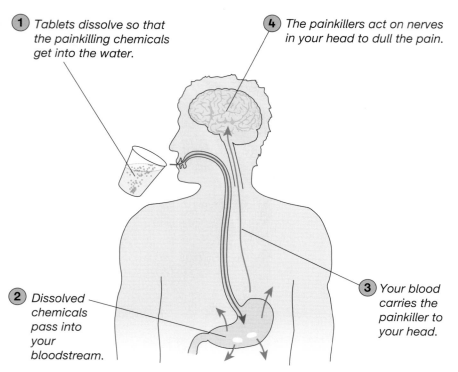

1 Tablets dissolve so that the painkilling chemicals get into the water.

4 The painkillers act on nerves in your head to dull the pain.

2 Dissolved chemicals pass into your bloodstream.

3 Your blood carries the painkiller to your head.

Dissolving speed and temperature

Temperature (°C)	Time to dissolve (secs)
5	39
10	29
15	20
20	18
25	15
30	13

Which form of medicine is best?

Medicine form	Advantages	Disadvantages
Tablets	Easy to supply the correct dose Easy to store	Takes time to dissolve in the body
Powder	Easy to supply correct dose	Needs to be taken with water Easy to spill
Liquid	Already dissolved so works very quickly	Difficult to make sure you get the correct dose without a measuring spoon Easy to spill
Injection	Medicine gets straight into the bloodstream	Needs to be done by a doctor Some people are very frightened of injections

Which brand of medicine is best?

Brand	How fast did it work?	How long did the effect last?	How easy to swallow?	Overall score
PainGo	5	3	3	4
PainRelief	3	4	4	3
SuperComfort	2	1	5	2
AcheLess	5	5	5	5
SootherPlus	5	4	2	3

5 = best, 1 = worst

Data response

1 List the things that must happen before a painkiller can cure your headache.

2 Give two advantages of tablets.

3 Give two disadvantages of injections.

4 What is the biggest disadvantage of SootherPlus?

5 Draw a chart to show the results for the speed at which the painkillers in the consumer test worked.

Research

6 Plan and carry out an investigation into the speed that tablets dissolve:
   - at different temperatures, or
   - with crushed or whole tablets.

   You will need to present your results using a barchart.

Presentation

7 Prepare a presentation for schools that show the dangers of fireworks. Do not include a lot of technical details about the reaction but do explain why the powder in the firework is dangerous.

Revision checklist

- The rates of chemical reactions varies. You can tell the difference between fast and slow reactions by looking. Barcharts can be used to show the speed of a reaction.

- A reaction stops when one of the reacting substances is used up.

- Increasing temperature usually speeds up chemical reactions. Lowering the temperature (in a refrigerator or freezer) slows down the changes that make food go bad.

- Increasing the concentration of the reacting chemicals increases the speed of a chemical reaction.

- The rate of reaction increases when small particles are used rather than large lumps. The larger surface area of the smaller particles allows more room for the reacting chemicals to get to each other.

- Catalysts are chemicals that speed up a reaction but are not used up in the reaction themselves. Different catalysts are needed for different reactions.

- Chemicals react when their atoms and molecules collide with each other. Anything that increases the number and speed of these collisions will increase the rate of reaction.

30.1 Gold dust

 How can we separate mixtures of substances?

You can find lumps of pure gold in rocks in Snowdonia, Wales. But how could you get it out?

One way is to grind the rocks and gold to a coarse powder. Then wash water through the mixture. The lighter rock particles are carried away but the heavy gold dust settles at the bottom.

So mixtures may contain substances that are useful. To get the useful substances from the mixture the mixture has to be separated into its different components. The method we use to **separate** out the mixture depends on the properties of the substances in the mix. How could you separate the tea flavour from the tea leaves?

Magnets are used to pull **magnetic** metals like iron or steel from a mixture. In this way food cans can be separated out from household rubbish for recycling.

Tea leaves settle to the bottom of the teapot. The liquid tea can then be poured off the top. This method of separating a solid from a liquid is called **decanting**

A tea bag lets water through but not the tea leaves. The tea bag act as a **filter**

Questions

1 Write a sentence that uses the word decant.

2 Gold is much heavier than rock. Explain how this helps people to find gold in a mixture of gold and rock.

3 Draw a flow chart to show how magnets could separate steel cans from plastic bottles.

4 Suggest one other way to separate plastic bottles from food cans.

5 Plan and test a way to get pure salt from rock salt.

Keywords

separate

magnetic

decant

filter

Sorting out

30.2 Faking it

 How does chromatography work?

Some people claim to have found a drawing left by aliens visiting Inca Temples. But is it really alien ink? We could use **chromatography** to check.

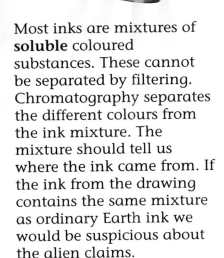

Most inks are mixtures of **soluble** coloured substances. These cannot be separated by filtering. Chromatography separates the different colours from the ink mixture. The mixture should tell us where the ink came from. If the ink from the drawing contains the same mixture as ordinary Earth ink we would be suspicious about the alien claims.

The **solvent** moves up the paper.

solvent front

As the solvent moves it separates the colours in the inks.

solvent

1 2 3 4 5 6 7 8

| 1–7 | Earth ink |
| 8 | Ink from drawing |

Questions

1 Write a sentence that uses the word solvent.

2 Do you think the drawing was made by aliens? How can you tell?

3 Name some substances that could be separated by chromatography.

4 Plan an experiment to find if the colours of Smarties are pure substances or mixtures.

5 If the ink came from Earth would that prove that the drawing was not made by aliens? Explain your reasons.

Keywords

chromatography
soluble
solvent

What separation techniques do doctors use?

Blood is a very complex **mixture**. Doctors use a **centrifuge** to separate cells from the blood, The centrifuge spins samples of blood around very fast. The cells settle at the bottom of the tube.

Kidney machines use a technique called **dialysis** to wash dissolved wastes from the blood. The blood is pumped along tubes made of a special material. The wastes pass through the material but the rest of the blood cannot. Special dialysis solution passing the other way carries away the wastes. The blood can then go back into the patient.

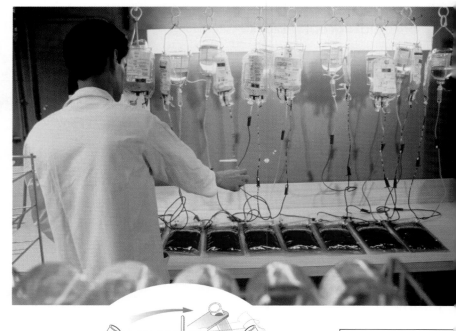

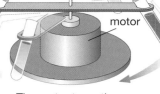

motor

The motor turns the rotary arm very fast.

Before spinning

blood cells and plasma

After spinning

clear pale yellow liquid above cells in each tube

dialysis tube

dirty blood from patient

white blood cell

watery solution carries away waste material

waste passes through membrane

red blood cells

clean blood to patient

Questions

1 What do hospitals use centrifuges for?

2 Which machine in a hospital uses dialysis?

3 What does this machine do?

4 Design a leaflet to explain to patients how the separation techniques used in hospitals work. Include the separation of blood products and dialysis.

5 Why does blood need to be pumped through the kidney machine?

Keywords

mixture

centrifuge

dialysis

Sorting out

30.4 Oil and whisky

How does fractional distillation work?

Some liquids mix so well that they look like a single substance. But even these mixtures can be separated. **Distillation** is a way to separate liquids with different boiling points.

Whisky makers distil a mixture to produce one liquid. This liquid is a mixture of alcohol, water and flavourings with 40% alcohol. This makes it eight times stronger than beer!

Oil companies use a similar technique for **crude oil**. However, the oil companies collect more than one type of liquid from the crude oil. These different liquids are called **fractions**. This is why this sort of distillation is called **fractional distillation**.

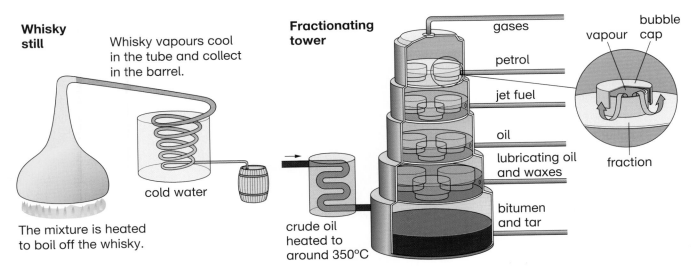

Whisky still

Whisky vapours cool in the tube and collect in the barrel.

cold water

The mixture is heated to boil off the whisky.

Fractionating tower

gases

petrol

jet fuel

oil

lubricating oil and waxes

bitumen and tar

crude oil heated to around 350°C

vapour — bubble cap

fraction

Questions

1 Write a sentence containing the word distillation.

2 Name two liquids that can be separated by fractional distillation.

3 What differences in two liquids does fractional distillation depend on to separate the liquids?

4 How can alcohol be separated from the water in wine?

5 Design a solar-powered still to separate freshwater from seawater.

Keywords

distillation
crude oil
fractions
fractional distillation

Rock salt prices per tonne

Premium	£2.30
Grade A	£2.00
Commercial	£1.50
Waste	57p

Pure salt manufacturing costs

Salt extraction	£20 per tonne of rock salt

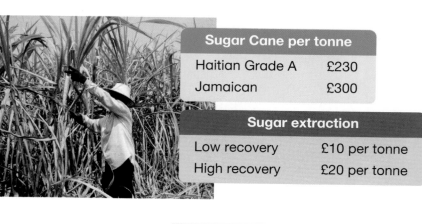

Sugar Cane per tonne

Haitian Grade A	£230
Jamaican	£300

Sugar extraction

Low recovery	£10 per tonne
High recovery	£20 per tonne

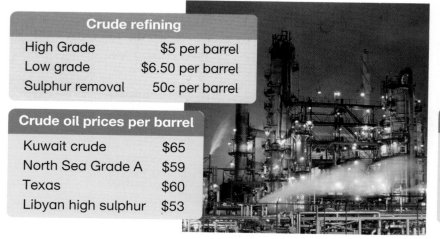

Crude refining

High Grade	$5 per barrel
Low grade	$6.50 per barrel
Sulphur removal	50c per barrel

Crude oil prices per barrel

Kuwait crude	$65
North Sea Grade A	$59
Texas	$60
Libyan high sulphur	$53

Coffee beans per 100 kg

Ethiopian High Mountain	£120
Jamaican	£90
Brazilian pure Arabica	£100
Brazilian blend	£85

Data response

1 How much does a tonne of Jamaican sugar cane cost?
2 How much would 23 barrels of North Sea Grade A oil cost?
3 Which is the most expensive coffee?
4 What is the process of separating pure salt from rock salt called?
5 One 100 kg of coffee beans produces enough instant coffee to fill 900 100g jars. How much instant coffee is this in total?

6 How much coffee is wasted when the beans are made into instant?

7 High recovery sugar extraction uses hot water. Low recovery uses cold water. Why does the high recovery method produce more pure sugar?

8 What do we call the process that separates crude oil into petrol and other useful products?

Research

9 Roasted coffee beans are ground into a rough powder and mixed with water to make coffee. Plan an investigation to see how finely ground you should make the powder to get the maximum amount of coffee flavour out.

10 Some people want to have coffee bags just like teabags. This would keep the grounds out of their drink. Plan an investigation to see what sort of fabric would be best for these coffee bags.

Presentation

11 There are many ways to separate mixtures: dissolving, filtering, chromatography, distillation, dialysis and magnetic sorting. Prepare a presentation to show how they work. Include pictures. Give examples of the kind of mixtures that can be separated by each method.

Respond • Research • Present

Revision checklist

I know

- A mixture contains two or more uncombined substances. Substances in mixtures can be separated from each other. To separate a soluble substance (e.g. salt, copper sulphate or sugar) from an insoluble substance (e.g. sand) dissolve the soluble substance and filter off the insoluble one. The soluble substance can be recovered from the solution by boiling.

- Chromatography separates mixtures depending on how well they dissolve in liquids and how fast they move along a piece of chromatography paper. In simple chromatograms the more soluble substances with lighter molecules move further up the chromatography paper.

- Magnets separate iron from a mixture of iron and aluminium. Filtering can separate a solid from a solution. Decanting can separate a solid in a suspension.

- Centrifuging can separate mixtures by spinning a sample around very fast. The heavier parts of the mixture settle towards the bottom of the tube. Doctors use centrifuging to separate cells from blood.

- Dialysis is used in kidney machines to clean wastes from the blood.

- Distillation can obtain fresh water from sea water. Distillation can separate liquids with different boiling points. Whisky manufacturers use distillation to produce very strong solution of alcohol. Oil refineries use fractional distillation to separate useful fuels and chemicals from crude oil.

31.1 Is it all rubbish?

 How can we deal with rubbish?

The problem with rubbish is that it's such a mixture of things that all need to be treated differently. Old food, kitchen waste and paper will **rot** easily. These are called **biodegradable**. Plastics, glass and metal will not rot. These are called **non-biodegradable**.

Much of the rubbish we make ends up in a hole in the ground. These holes are often old quarries. They are filled up then covered with soil. They are called **landfill** sites.

Landfill sites may sound like a good idea. The rubbish is covered up and out of the way. However, we are running out of holes to fill. Another problem is that the biodegradable rubbish rots. This produces **methane** gas. The methane rises through the soil and can collect in buildings above ground. A spark can make the methane and air mixture explode.

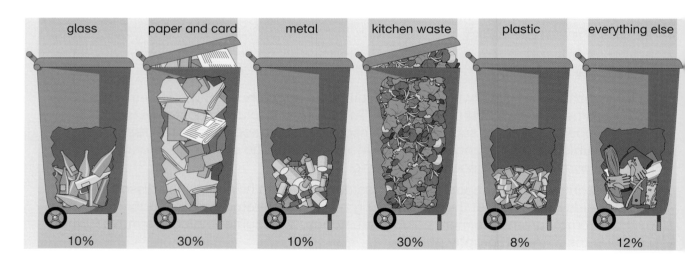

glass	paper and card	metal	kitchen waste	plastic	everything else
10%	30%	10%	30%	8%	12%

Questions

1 Write a sentence containing the word biodegradable.

2 Sort the rubbish in the diagram into biodegradable and non-biodegradable items.

3 Which gas is made in landfill sites?

4 What must be mixed with this gas before an explosion can take place?

5 Methane gas has no smell. Why does this make it extra dangerous?

Keywords

biodegradable

rot

non-biodegradable

landfill

methane

Rubbish

31.2 Fuel's gold!

How can we use rubbish?

We will never run out of rubbish. In fact, each year we are producing more! Rubbish could be a **renewable fuel**. Two bins of rubbish contain the same energy as one bag of coal.

Byker Reclamation Plant in Newcastle-upon-Tyne makes **fuel pellets** from rubbish. It makes 8 000 tonnes of fuel pellets each year. These can be sold for burning in solid fuel stoves.

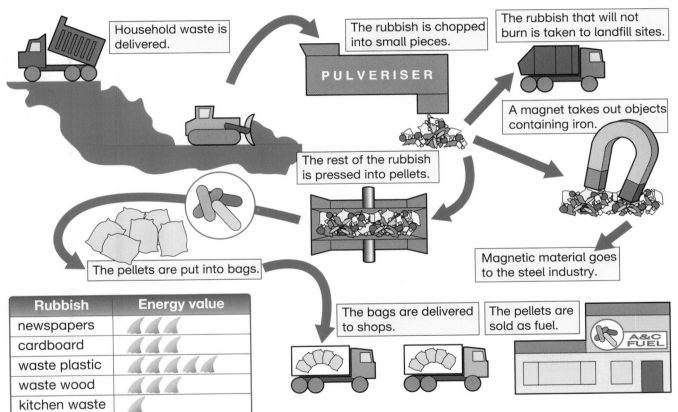

Household waste is delivered.

The rubbish is chopped into small pieces.

PULVERISER

The rubbish that will not burn is taken to landfill sites.

A magnet takes out objects containing iron.

The rest of the rubbish is pressed into pellets.

Magnetic material goes to the steel industry.

The pellets are put into bags.

The bags are delivered to shops.

The pellets are sold as fuel.

A&C FUEL

Rubbish	Energy value
newspapers	⚡⚡⚡
cardboard	⚡⚡⚡
waste plastic	⚡⚡⚡⚡⚡
waste wood	⚡⚡⚡
kitchen waste	⚡

Questions

1. Write a sentence using the word renewable.
2. Sort the following into things which can be used to make fuel pellets and things which cannot: cardboard; china; cloth; glass; metals; paper; plastic.
3. Draw a bar chart to show the energy in different types of rubbish.
4. List the advantages and disadvantages of using rubbish as a fuel.
5. Draw a design for a cooker that would use rubbish pellets as fuel. How would it be different from a normal gas cooker?

31.3 Just dump it?

What are the four Rs?

Most of the stuff we throw out as rubbish is not really rubbish at all. Before you put anything in the bin think about the 4 Rs.

Reduce the amount of materials you are throwing away. Do not take all the packaging they offer you in shops. Avoid products with lots of complex (and expensive!) packaging.

Reuse things – don't just throw them out! Repairing things is often cheaper than buying new. And you can always use old jars and tins to keep things in. What can you think of to reuse?

Recycle the materials – glass and newspaper is easy to recycle. But you can also recycle most metals, some plastics and many types of clothing.

Recover energy in rubbish by burning it. Byker Reclamation Plant in Newcastle does this. The energy is not wasted and we save valuable oil.

Questions

1 What are the four Rs?

2 List three things that are easy to recycle.

3 Give two reasons why you should avoid products with lots of packaging.

4 List the things you recycle at home.

5 Suggest three things you could easily do at home to help the environment.

Keywords

reduce
reuse
recycle
recover

31.4 Cradle to grave

Where do mobile phones go to die?

A new mobile phone! For a while it's your best friend, then a new model comes out and it's thrown away. We change our phones every two years or so. What happens to all those dead mobiles? And what does it take to make and dispose of a mobile phone?

All steps in the manufacture, use and disposal of a mobile phone affect the environment. Looking at all of these stages is called a **cradle to grave** analysis. We now need to look at ways to save energy and reduce pollution at each of these stages. Or maybe we could just keep our mobile phones for longer!

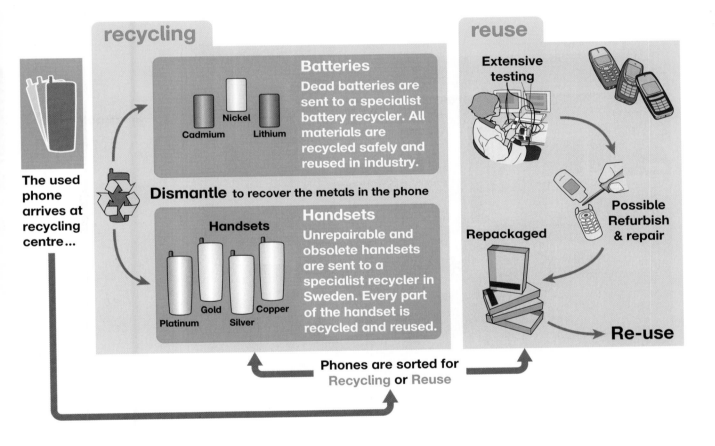

The used phone arrives at recycling centre...

recycling

Batteries
Dead batteries are sent to a specialist battery recycler. All materials are recycled safely and reused in industry.

Nickel
Cadmium   Lithium

Dismantle to recover the metals in the phone

Handsets
Unrepairable and obsolete handsets are sent to a specialist recycler in Sweden. Every part of the handset is recycled and reused.

Handsets
Gold   Copper
Platinum   Silver

reuse

Extensive testing

Possible Refurbish & repair

Repackaged

Re-use

Phones are sorted for **Recycling** or **Reuse**

Questions

1 List the metals found in mobile phone batteries.
2 What is a 'cradle to grave' analysis?
3 Why is it better to reuse a mobile phone rather than recycle it?
4 What happens to parts of the phone that cannot be reused or recycled?
5 Assume you change your mobile phone every two years. How many phones will you get through by the age of 70?

Keywords
cradle to grave
recycle
cadmium
reuse

31 Data response: Collecting rubbish

Mass of different types of rubbish (kg) for one household in the first 13 weeks of 2006

	Date of rubbish collection												
	Jan 6	Jan 13	Jan 20	Jan 27	Feb 3	Feb 10	Feb 17	Feb 24	Mar 3	Mar 10	Mar 17	Mar 26	Apr 3
Metal	150	250	110	200	115	100	95	25	119	165	133	125	100
Plastics	200	450	190	210	220	170	150	50	185	200	140	180	150
Glass	350	750	220	230	100	175	100	50	350	250	230	290	300
Paper	750	1250	600	700	630	590	650	150	760	650	700	750	690
Garden waste	0	0	0	0	0	0	0	0	0	0	0	2500	750
Food waste	850	1200	900	790	860	800	950	200	1050	700	850	750	900
Everything else	700	850	650	670	500	600	730	260	950	800	640	700	490
Totals	3000	4750	2670	2800	2425	2435	2675	735	3414	2765	2693	5295	3380

John's birthday party 11th Jan

Paris trip Feb 19th to 23rd

Data response

1 Which week had the highest total weight of rubbish?

2 Which week had the lowest glass waste?

3 What was the highest value for paper thrown out in one week?

4 What is the total weight of rubbish for the week beginning March 10th?

5 How can you explain the amount of paper and food thrown out on Jan 13th?

6 How did the trip to Paris affect the amount of rubbish thrown out on Feb 24th?

7 One weekend the householders did a lot of gardening. When do you think they did this? Why?

Rubbish

8 Keep a 'rubbish diary' for one week to see what sorts of things you are throwing away. Sort your rubbish into groups like biodegradable, plastics, metals, glass and so on to see how much of each type your family is producing.

Present your data in a poster or chart for your class to see.

Presentation

Recycling is a waste of energy! You drive for miles to take a few bottles to the tip – it does more harm to the environment than just throwing them in the bin!

We must recycle – it makes environmental sense. It means we use less and we have less to get rid of.

9 Prepare a presentation to support either of these viewpoints. You will need to do some research to find some facts and figures to back up their statements.

Revision checklist

I know:

● Landfill, burning, recycling and composting are used to get rid of rubbish.

● Paper, wood, cotton and vegetable matter are called biodegradable and will rot away. Most plastics and glass are non-biodegradable and will not rot. Methane gas from landfill sites can be used as a fuel but can also be an explosion hazard.

● Burning rubbish produces ash, waste gases and energy. Some rubbish can be made into fuel pellets.

● Recycling materials saves natural resources (including energy) and reduces disposal problems.

● The four Rs are: reduce, reuse, recycle and recover. Reducing means using less, particularly unnecessary packaging. Reusing means repairing things rather than throwing them away or using things in new ways, for example a tin can as a flower vase. Recycling means using the materials something is made from again. For example we can recycle glass or paper quite easily to make new glass bottles and newspapers. Recovering means burning the rubbish to get back some of the energy it contains to heat homes, workplaces and generate electricity.

● Metals (such as iron) and glass are easier to recycle than plastics because there are so many types of plastics which need to be treated in different ways.

● The cradle to grave analysis looks at all of the stages in a product's lifecycle.

32.1 Black, sticky and smelly

How can we get useful materials from crude oil?

It's sticky, smelly and doesn't burn easily. It's also **toxic** which means it can kill living things. But **crude oil** is one of the most useful chemical mixtures on the planet.

Fuels

Fractional distillation separates crude oil into different more useful **fractions**. The Buncefield Oil Depot fire in December 2005 lasted three days and needed 600 firefighters to control it. It was large enough to be seen from space! But it was not oil that was burning – it was mainly diesel, petrol and kerosene.

Fraction	Boiling point (°C)	Uses
Petroleum gases	Less than 65	Bottled gas for camping or portable heaters
Petrol and diesel	75–150	Fuel to make our road vehicles work
Kerosene	250–300	Fuel for jet engines
Lubricating oil and waxes	320–450	Lubricating oils help to protect engines. Waxes can be used for candles and waterproofing fabrics
Bitumen and tar	More than 500	Mixed with small stones these can make garden paths and even roads

Questions

1 Write a sentence with the word toxic in it.

2 What is the boiling point range for petrol and diesel?

3 Which fraction has a boiling point in the range 250–300°C?

4 Give an example of a fraction from crude oil that does not burn easily.

5 Why is crude oil such a useful mixture?

Keywords

toxic

crude oil

fractional distillation

fractions

32.2 Spot the killer!

 What gas is made when methane burns?

Which of the pictures above shows a real murderer? Well, it's not Dracula! The fire is a real killer though. It burns **methane** gas to heat water. If it has plenty of air and is properly adjusted this is completely safe. It makes **carbon dioxide** and water vapour.

> Gas + **oxygen** → carbon dioxide + water vapour

If there is not enough air a different reaction takes place. This time small amounts of **poisonous carbon monoxide** are produced as well. This poisons the red blood cells and stops them carrying oxygen to the cells of the body. Carbon monoxide poisoning can kill you.

> Gas + less oxygen → carbon dioxide + water vapour + carbon monoxide

This small piece of plastic could save your life. It changes colour if carbon monoxide is present, warning you to have your gas appliances serviced or replaced.

Questions

1 What gas is made when fuels burn in plenty of oxygen?

2 What gas is made when fuels burn without enough oxygen?

3 Carbon monoxide is colourless and has no smell. Why does this make it particularly dangerous?

4 What is the chemical name of natural gas?

5 Design a poster to warn people of the dangers of carbon monoxide poisoning.

Keywords

methane

carbon dioxide

oxygen

poisonous

carbon monoxide

32.3 Petrol or diesel?

Which is the best fuel for cars?

Petrol gives you better acceleration and a faster top speed. It costs a bit more per tankful but cars with diesel engines cost more in the first place. And after a few thousand miles your diesel car will begin to sound like a white van!

*Petrol is much more expensive and modern **diesel** engines are now as good as petrol ones. If you keep it serviced regularly it will still sound sweet when it's done 90 000 miles – or at least no worse than a petrol engine! You also get more miles to the gallon. What's to dislike?*

Fuels

Car	VW Golf Sport 1.9 Diesel	VW Golf Sport 1.6 Petrol
Engine size (cc)	1896	1600
Fuel **consumption**		
Urban cycle (mpg)	37.7	27.2
Other driving (mpg)	58.9	45.6
Engine emissions (g/km)	157	185
Engine noise levels (dB)	69	74
Acceleration 0–62 mph (secs)	11.2	11.5
Price in December 2005 (£)	17 630	16 445

Questions

1 What mileage do you get from a diesel engine in the urban cycle?

2 What is the difference in price between the two cars in the table?

3 Give three advantages of diesel engines.

4 Give three advantages of petrol engines.

5 Would you buy a diesel or petrol car? Why?

Keywords

petrol

acceleration

diesel

consumption

Yak burners

⇨ **What is the best fuel to boil water?**

It's brown, sticky and comes out of yaks. And it's a great **fuel**! There are very few trees in Tibet so the local people collect yak **faeces** for fuel. They shape it into pancakes and dry them out on the rocks. When they need some heat for cooking they just throw a yak patty on the fire! But the most important question is – how much heat does it give out when it burns?

Cooking method	Time to boil enough water for tea	Ease of use	Cost
Yak stove	5 min 45 sec	★★	2
Wood stove	4 min 5 sec	★★★	3
Electric cooker	4 min 15 sec	★★★★★	5
Gas cooker	4 min 55 sec	★★★★★	3
Solar kettle	10 min 47 sec	★★★	1

Questions

1 Which cooker boiled water the quickest?

2 Which cooker is the most expensive to run?

3 What is the biggest disadvantage of the solar kettle?

4 How long would it take to boil twice as much water on a yak stove?

5 What is the main advantage of yak faeces as a fuel?

Keywords

fuel

faeces

32 Data response: Cooking at camp

David did an experiment in science before he went camping to find out which fuel was best.

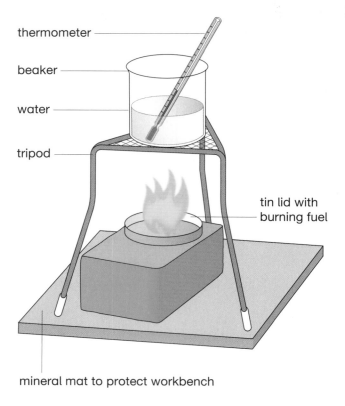

thermometer

beaker

water

tripod

tin lid with
burning fuel

mineral mat to protect workbench

60p – burns for 30 mins

£1.20p – burns for 2 hours

97p – burns for 2 hours

£6.00 – burns for 2 hours

Fuel	Time to boil 100 ml water (secs)
Ethanol	134
Firelighter block	130
Hexamine	122
Camping gaz	90

Fuels

1 How long did it take to boil the water with hexamine?

2 Which fuel gave out the most heat?

3 David was careful to start with the same amount of water at the same temperature every time. Why?

4 David did not measure how much fuel was used each time. Does this matter? Why?

5 Think of a way that David could measure how much of each fuel was needed to boil the water.

6 What is the cost per minute to burn firelighters?

7 What is the cost per minute to burn camping gas?

Research

8 Using a spirit lamp look at the effect of a silver foil chimney on the way the smoke moves. If the chimney is near the flame does it suck the smoke upwards? How does the size and shape of the chimney affect the smoke movement?

Presentation

9 Prepare a brochure for a car manufacturer to advertise their cars. The same car is available with a petrol or a diesel engine. The brochure must stress the good points about each type of fuel and engine. Include lots of photographs and make both cars look exciting!

Revision checklist

I know:

- Crude oil is a toxic, dark sticky liquid. It is a mixture that is separated into more useful parts at an oil refinery by fractional distillation. Petroleum gases, petrol, kerosene and diesel come from crude oil. Some fuels ignite more easily than others.

- Petroleum gases, such as propane, are used in portable gas cylinders for heaters and cookers. Petrol and diesel is used in cars. Kerosene is used in aeroplanes. Diesel is used in lorries, buses, trains and some cars.

- Burning fuels produce energy for heating, transport and making electricity in power stations.

- Carbon monoxide forms when fuels from crude oil burn in a limited supply of air. Carbon monoxide is a poisonous, colourless gas with no smell.

- Petrol gives better acceleration but costs more than diesel in cars. Diesel gives more miles per gallon but needs more expensive engines than petrol. Which fuel people use in their motor vehicles is a personal choice.

Respond • Research • Present

33.1 Food additives

 Why do we use food additives?

Look what happens when an apple is exposed to the air. But one side has been treated with lemon juice to prevent it turning brown. Fruit juice is a simple natural food **additive**.

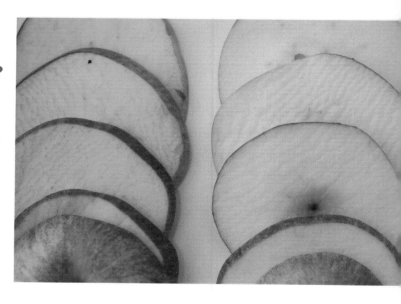

Some people are keen to avoid any additives in their foods – especially artificial ones. They say they are all bad and best avoided. What is added to food and why?

Additives	What do they do?	Some common examples
Antioxidants	Help to preserve the food and stop it going off	Vitamin C is added to many juices.
Flavour enhancers	Make the food taste better	**Monosodium glutamate** is sometimes added to Chinese food. Ordinary table salt also makes many foods taste better.
Food colours	Make the food look better Replace colours that fade when the food is processed	Peas would look greyish green and tinned strawberries would go brown if they did not have added colour.

Mixtures of oil and water can separate out into two layers, making the food look unattractive or spoil. **Emulsifiers** are additives that stop this happening. Salad dressing often contains emulsifiers to keep it smooth.

Questions

1 What are the three main types of food additives?

2 Why are flavour enhancers added to food?

3 What would tinned strawberries look like without the added colours?

4 What does an emulsifier do?

5 What sorts of foods contain emulsifiers?

Keywords

additive

emulsifiers

antioxidant

monosodium glutamate

Food chemicals

33.2 Crisps

> **Why is oxygen a problem for crisps?**

Crisps react quickly with the air. The **moisture** makes them soggy and the oxygen makes them go off. Manufacturers fill crisp packets with **nitrogen** gas, not air. The lack of oxygen means the crisps stay fresh for months. The nitrogen gas is also treated to be quite dry. This stops the crisps going soggy.

What happens with crisps also happens with other foods. **Oxygen** in the air attacks the food and makes it go off. In a world where some people do not have enough to eat this is a terrible waste. Food additives and simple packaging help to preserve food.

But how can we be sure all these additives are safe? We should not be eating them?

Before any additive is allowed in food it has to be tested. In the UK you see E numbers for food additives. Before anything gets an E number it must pass safety tests – so an E number is actually good news! **E300** may sound a bit frightening – but it's the number for vitamin C!

Questions

1 What stops crisps going off in the packet?
2 What is the gas in the air that spoils many foods?
3 How can we help to stop food spoiling?
4 What has to happen to a food additive before it can get an E number?
5 What is the common name for E300?

Keywords

moisture
nitrogen
oxygen
E300

33.3 Vitamins

 What are vitamins?

Vitamins are chemicals that help to keep us healthy. We only need very small amounts of vitamins – but we need them every day. A healthy **diet** gives us all we need – but not if we just eat burgers and chips every day! There are about 15 vitamins but the one most people know is **vitamin C**. This helps to keep skin and gums healthy. It also makes wounds and cuts heal more quickly. Vitamin C is found in oranges, other fruits and green vegetables.

Person	Freddie	Mina	Shaun	Megan
Breakfast	Toast and jam, coffee	Toast and marmalade, fresh orange juice	Can of fizzy drink on the way to school	Can of fizzy drink on the way to school
Lunch	Pizza slice, can of fizzy drink	Sandwiches (cheese salad), can of fizzy drink	Sausage roll and chips	Pizza slice
Dinner	Spaghetti bolognaise, fruit pie and custard	Meat pie, potatoes and broccoli	Beans on toast, chocolate ice cream	Fish and chips from the shop
Any snacks	Chocolate bar at break	Apple at break	Orange	Packet of crisps, bar of chocolate

Questions

1. What are vitamins?
2. List three foods that contain plenty of vitamin C.
3. Which person is most likely to have a good supply of vitamin C in their diet?
4. Which person is most likely to have very little vitamin C in their diet?
5. What advice would you give to someone who has a low level of vitamin C?

Keywords

vitamins

diet

vitamin C

33.4 More tea sir?

How much sugar do you eat every day?

Some people add **sugar** to tea or coffee to make it sweeter. But it is added to many other foods as well. Fizzy drinks, cakes, biscuits, tomato ketchup, chicken burgers and mayonnaise all contain sugar! The average teenager in Britain takes in 81 g of sugar every day added to foods and drinks – that's 29 bags of sugar every year! This is probably too high for good health. Sugars help to cause **tooth decay**. Too much sugar also makes you fat.

Some **slimming** foods and diet drinks contain **artificial sweeteners** like **aspartame** instead of sugar. These make the food taste sweet but do not contain the calories of sugar or cause tooth decay. Unfortunately, some people react badly to these artificial sweeteners. Other people do not like the taste.

Questions

1 List the foods you have eaten today that contain sugar.
2 Give two reasons why too much sugar is bad for you.
3 Why do some foods contain artificial sweeteners instead of sugar?
4 How much sugar does the average teenager in the UK take in every day?
5 Think of three ways you could cut down your sugar intake.

Keywords

sugar

tooth decay

slimming

artificial sweetener

aspartame

33 Data response: Crazy food colours

The colour of food has an important effect on the way we taste it. People were asked to identify a faint taste by licking different coloured pieces of flavoured paper. The table below shows the percentage of people who got the answers right.

Percentage of correct guesses

Colour	Mint flavour	Banana flavour	Apple flavour
Yellow	68	85	60
Green	95	70	85
Red	55	65	75
Blue	95	70	45
Black	75	75	50
Brown	65	85	70

A company tested two strawberry jams on members of the public. Both jams were exactly the same – but one had red colouring. The graph shows which jam people preferred.

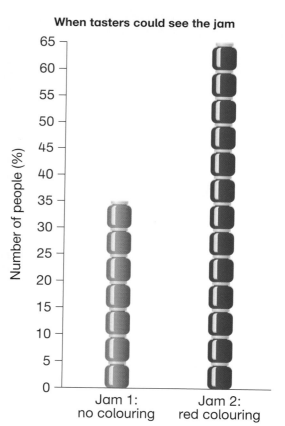

When tasters could see the jam

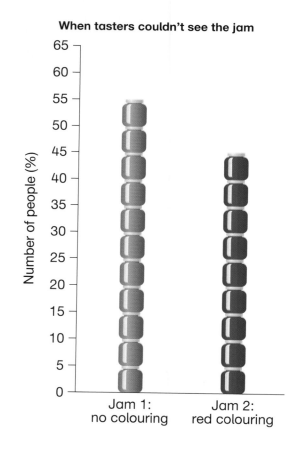

When tasters couldn't see the jam

Data response

1 Which colour gives the most accurate result for mint?

2 Which colour is worst for banana?

3 With which colour did only 55% of the people guess the flavour correctly?

4 When the same test was done blindfolded so that people could not see the colours the results actually improved! Why do you think this was?

5 Which flavour is easiest to detect?

6 Which jam did people prefer in the first taste test?

7 How can you explain the result from the taste test?

Research

8 A chemical called DCPIP changes colour from blue to colourless when it reacts with vitamin C. This is used to find out how much vitamin C is present in food. The more DCPIP that goes clear the more vitamin C is present.

Plan and carry out an investigation to see how cooking affects the level of vitamin C in foods like cauliflower or green vegetables.

Presentation

9 People spend a fortune on foods that contain 'no artificial additives'. Often these foods go stale or mouldy before the ones containing additives! Design a poster to show the benefits of food additives. The poster should be colourful, large and suitable for display in a shop.

Revision checklist

I know:

- Some foods contain chemicals called additives added by people. The main types of food additives are antioxidants, flavour enhancers and food colours.

- Food additives only have an E number if they have been tested for safety. Some additives can be harmful to some people.

- Flavour enhancers help to make food taste better. Food colours change the colour – often when the colour has been changed by processing.

- Oxygen from the air makes food go off. Antioxidants preserve food by stopping the effects of oxygen in the air.

- Chemicals called emulsifiers help to make a mixture with one part spread in fine specks or droplets through another. They are used to make food products such as salad dressing and mayonnaise.

- Vitamins are chemicals that we need in small amounts every day to keep us healthy. The amount we need every day is called the Recommended Daily Allowance (RDA) of a vitamin.

- Sugar is a sweetener. It is also used in many foods that do not always taste sweet to us. Too much sugar in the diet can cause tooth decay and make you fat. Diet drinks and some slimming foods contain artificial sweeteners instead of sugar.

34.1 Planetary rubbish

 How did the solar system form?

The **Solar System** is about 4.6 billion years old. It started when dust and rock orbiting the Sun joined together to form the **planets** and their **moons**. The planets and moons reflect light from the Sun. This means that we can see them easily with telescopes.

But some of the dust and rock did not go into the planets. This left-over rubbish forms asteroids and comets. **Asteroids** are made from rock and most of them orbit the Sun in an area called the asteroid belt. Asteroids can be as small as a family car – or as big as Mount Everest!

Comets are mixtures of ice and rock. These tend to travel through space not in orbits. Comets are usually smaller than asteroids. **Meteorites** are even smaller. Objects falling through the Earth's atmosphere are called meteorites. A comet can become a meteorite as it falls and melts.

The diagram shows the planets of the solar system.

Questions

1 When did the Solar System form?
2 What is an asteroid made from?
3 Where do you find most asteroids?
4 What is the difference between asteroids and comets?
5 Planets do not give out light like the sun. How can we see them?

Keywords

Solar System
planet
moon
asteroid
comet
meteorite

Deep impact

34

In the diagram, the planets are labelled from the Sun outwards: Sun, Mercury, Venus, Earth, Mars, Jupiter, Saturn, Uranus, Neptune, Pluto.

34.2 Craters

 How do craters form?

The **Moon** is a giant lump of rock orbiting the Earth at about 250 000 miles. It reflects light from the Sun. The surface is covered with **craters** made when asteroids crashed into it. There is no **atmosphere** on the Moon so even the smallest asteroids get through to the surface. The size of the crater depends on the mass and speed of the asteroid.

The Moon may be the remains of a planet that collided with the Earth millions of years ago. It was caught in the Earth's gravitational field and is still trapped orbiting around us.

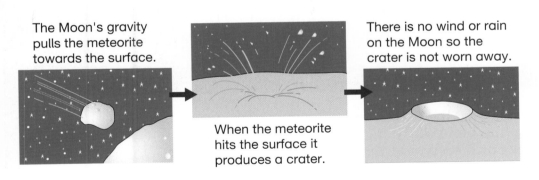

The Moon's gravity pulls the meteorite towards the surface.

When the meteorite hits the surface it produces a crater.

There is no wind or rain on the Moon so the crater is not worn away.

Questions

1 What is the Moon made from?

2 How far away is the Moon?

3 How do we know that the Moon has been hit by many asteroids?

4 What affects the size of a crater made by an asteroid?

5 Light comes to us from the Moon – but where does it come from originally?

Keywords

Moon

crater

atmosphere

34.3 End of the world?

 Did an asteroid strike kill off the dinosaurs?

An **asteroid** measuring 10 km across hit the Earth about 50 million years ago. It exploded with the same force as millions of tons of high explosive. Everything within 500 km was destroyed instantly. Trillions of tonnes of dust, gases and water vapour were shot into the atmosphere and cut the light reaching the surface. The average temperature dropped dramatically. The shock wave set fire to forests over 1000 km away. The waters in the oceans were churned up and the floating plants died. The fish that fed on them died. And then the acid gases from the burning forests were washed into the oceans by the rain.

We can still see the remains of a **crater** from an asteroid strike from millions of years ago in the Arizona desert.

At the time dinosaurs roamed the Earth – today not one of them is left. Could humans go the same way if an asteroid hit today? In fact, meteorites hit the Earth every day. But they are small and burn up as they fall through the atmosphere. We see these as shooting stars.

Deep impact

Questions

1 What is an asteroid made from?
2 How big was the asteroid that hit the Earth 50 million years ago?
3 List three things that happened when the asteroid hit the Earth.
4 Why are shooting stars not dangerous?
5 How can scientists detect asteroids heading towards the Earth?

Keywords

asteroid

crater

34.4 Near Earth Objects

➡️ **Can we protect the planet from asteroids?**

In the 1998 film *Armageddon,* an asteroid is heading towards the Earth. Scientists predict it will hit unless something is done. But how can we protect ourselves?

Bruce Willis to the rescue! He pilots a spaceship to meet the asteroid while it is still some way off and blows it up with nuclear bombs. This does not destroy the asteroid but **deflects** it so that it misses us. Thanks Bruce!

Asteroids that pass near the Earth are called **Near Earth Objects** or **NEOs**. A very heavy NEO is difficult to deflect but a lighter NEO can be pushed aside by a small explosion. Scientists can tell the **mass** of an asteroid by how easily it can be deflected by gravity or explosions.

Questions

1 What is a Near Earth Object?
2 Which NEOs will be the most dangerous? Why?
3 How could we deflect a NEO?
4 Why are some people worried about NEOs?
5 If a giant NEO was going to hit the Earth would you want to know?

Keywords

deflect
Near Earth Object
NEO
mass

34 Data response: What's the chance of that?

The NEOs detected by NASA in early 2006

Name	Most likely impact years	Chance of impact (1 in)	Speed per (km per sec-1)	Diameter (km)	Torino risk
2004 MN4	2036–2037	625 000	5.87	0.32	1
2005 WY55	2053–2057	7 692 308	18.7	0.25	0
2006 AL8	2102–2102	196 078 431	34.95	0.72	0
2006 AR3	2085–2085	163 934 426	12.82	0.29	0
2005 WG57	2029–2104	20 408 163	9.91	0.06	0
2005 XA8	2063–2086	1 265 823	12.08	0.03	0
2005 YU55	2036–2101	138 888 889	13.53	0.13	0
2005 YR3	2058–2085	9 090 909 091	6.5	0.068	0
2006 BO7	2060–2060	500 000 000	9.83	0.005	0
2005 WN3	2024–2024	3 333 333 333	18.17	0.004	0
1997 XR2	2101–2101	1 030 928	7	0.23	1

Chances of winning the UK lottery

Prize	Chance of winning
Jackpot	1 in 13 983 816
5+bonus	1 in 2 330 636
5-match	1 in 55 491
4-match	1 in 1032
3-match	1 in 57

Torino scale of likely damage

0	No risk of collision
2	Unlikely to hit the Earth and if it did would cause almost no impact.
4	A 1 in 100 chance of hitting the Earth. Could cause some damage.
6	A close encounter – but no certainty of hitting the Earth. Would cause a lot of damage if it did.
8	The NEO will hit the Earth. Will cause damage and possibly a tsunami if it lands on the oceans.
10	The NEO will hit the Earth and could cause massive damage with considerable loss of life.

Deep impact

Data response

1 What is the speed of 2006 AR3?

2 What is the diameter of 2005 YR3?

3 Are any of the NEOs discovered by NASA in 2006 larger than 1 km?

4 When will 2006 AR3 pass near the Earth?

5 A NEO could cause a lot of damage – but we are not yet certain it will hit the Earth. Which torino number would it have?

6 Which is more likely – winning the jackpot in the UK lottery or the Earth being hit by 2005 WY55?

Research

7 Plan an investigation to see how the mass of a marble affects the size of the crater it makes in a tray of sand.

Presentation

8 Tracking asteroids in deep space is expensive. Prepare a presentation for the United Nation's science committee about the dangers of Near Earth Objects. Your presentation should aim to convince them that they need to spend money on NEO tracking.

Revision checklist

I know:

- The damage done by moving objects depends on their speed and mass.

- Asteroids and comets move through space and may hit the Earth and Moon or other planets. This causes craters which we can see clearly on the Moon.

- The Moon orbits the Earth. It has no atmosphere. The Moon and planets in the Solar System reflect light from the Sun. The Moon may be the remains of a planet which collided with Earth millions of years ago.

- Asteroids are rocks left over from the formation of the Solar System. Comets are lumps of dust and ice. A comet falling into the Earth's atmosphere is called a meteorite.

- A Near Earth Object (NEO) is an asteroid or comet that may hit the Earth or pass quite close. Scientists track the movement of an asteroid across the distant sky with telescopes. They can calculate its likely path but the further away it is the more difficult it is to predict accurately whether it will hit us or not.

- A large asteroid hitting the Earth would cause an explosion bigger than an atomic bomb. It has happened in the past and probably caused the extinction of the dinosaurs. The explosion would send shock waves around the planet and cause fires and changes to the atmosphere and oceans. It is possible that all human life would be destroyed.

Sound effects

35.1 The Sound of Music!

👉 **How do instruments make sounds?**

A band will use lots of different instruments during a concert. The **sound** is very loud. You can often feel the **beat** of the music in your stomach.

We make sounds in many different ways. They all depend on transferring **energy**. The more energy there is the louder the **volume** will be. The energy is carried by **vibrations** that can travel through gases, liquids and solids.

When a string vibrates on a musical instrument it pushes against the air on every side of it. This sets up **waves** in the air. They travel in every direction and we hear these tiny vibrations as sounds.

Questions

1 What do the words 'sound wave' mean?

2 Make a list of musical instruments.

3 Sort your list into stringed instruments, wind instruments and drums.

4 Plan an investigation to find out how changing the length of a plucked string changes the note. If you can, carry out your investigation.

Keywords

sound

beat

energy

volume

vibration

wave

35.2 The recording studio

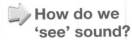

How do we 'see' sound?

Every band wants to sign a record contract and make a single. If they are lucky, they will go on to have a huge hit. However, most bands don't make it this far!

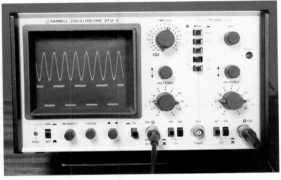

This machine is an **oscilloscope**. It shows sound vibrations as waves. The louder the sound is, the taller the wave. The height of the wave is called the **amplitude**.

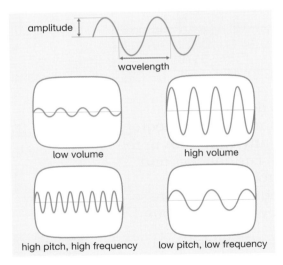

An oscilloscope also shows the pitch of the note. If the note is low pitched the wave is long; if it is high pitched the wave is short. This is called the **wavelength**. The **frequency** is the number of wavelengths that you can fit into one second. Notes with a long wavelength have a low frequency and notes with a short wavelength have a high frequency.

Questions

1 What does the word 'frequency' mean?
2 Draw a sound wave. Label it with the words amplitude and wavelength.
3 A recording studio allows people to tour the studio from time to time. Design a brochure telling them what they might see.
4 Draw some high frequency sound waves.
5 If you were told you had a low-pitched voice what would this mean?

Keywords

oscilloscope
amplitude
wavelength
frequency

35.3 Whale song

 What is the speed of sound?

Some people listen to recordings of dolphins and whales making noises. They claim this helps them to relax. Some parents use these recordings to help their babies sleep.

Dolphins hear because sound travels through the water. Sound vibrations can travel through gases, liquids and solids. Space is a **vacuum**. In a vacuum there is nothing to vibrate so sound cannot travel.

Sound waves can be **reflected**. We call this an **echo**. Sounds reflect best from hard surfaces. Bats use echoes to judge distances. Ships use **echo sounding** to find the depth of the sea.

Depth of sea = $\frac{1}{2}$ time × speed of sound in water

Substance	Speed of sound (m per sec)
Air	330
Water	1500
Steel	5170

We can also detect sounds travelling in rocks. A seismograph can pick up tiny vibrations in the Earth's crust. Earthquakes and volcanoes produce these vibrations. Some of them are so powerful they travel all around the world.

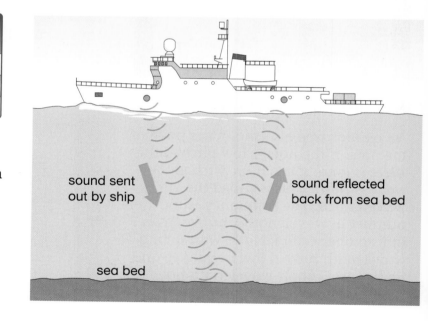

sound sent out by ship

sound reflected back from sea bed

sea bed

Questions

1 What is an echo?

2 A ship is using echo sounding to find the depth of the sea. The ship sends out a sound and receives the echo after two seconds. Use the formula above to calculate the depth of the sea.

3 Plan an experiment to measure the speed of sound in air.

4 What sorts of sounds can a seismograph detect?

5 Why does sound seem louder in the bathroom than in the living room?

Keywords

vacuum

reflect

echo

echo sounding

35.4 Turn it down!

How do we measure the loudness of sound?

Jet engines make a lot of noise. Imagine the noise when you put one inside a car and stand next to it! This **sound meter** is measuring the sound produced by a jet car at a safe distance. It's still over 110 **decibels**!

Very loud sounds can be harmful. They can strain the delicate parts of your ear. After listening to loud music it takes time for your ears to recover. Never turn up your MP3 player to drown out the background noise – if it's loud enough to do that it's probably loud enough to damage your ears.

0	20	40	60	80	100	120	140	decibels
no sound	quiet library	whisper	telephone ringing	door slamming	loud car horn	pneumatic drill	pain and ear damage	

	×4	×15	×60	×250	×1000	×4000	×8000	how many times louder

Questions

1 How loud is a sound of 10 decibels?

2 Why should people who work with noisy machines wear ear protectors?

3 Design a poster to show the causes and problems of noise pollution.

4 Why should you never turn your MP3 player up to full volume?

Keywords

sound meter

decibel

35 Data response: Noise pollution

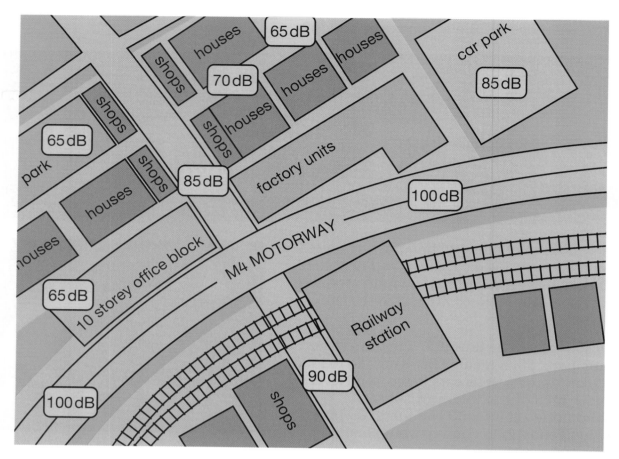

The map shows the noise levels in different London streets. Is anywhere too noisy?

The photograph shows a live band in a street in Amsterdam on Queen's Day. There is much less traffic in Amsterdam so it is quiet enough for live gigs to celebrate the Queen's birthday!

Data response

1 Which area has the loudest background noise?

2 How can you explain this?

3 Which area is quietest?

4 How can you explain this?

5 Which area has a noise level of 90 dB?

6 The Flying Pig is a pub where loud rock bands often play. They have been warned that they will lose their licence if the noise level goes above 100 dB for three nights in a row. Look at the data for Christmas and New Year 2005. Will they lose their licence?

Date	Dec 18	Dec 19	Dec 20	Dec 21	Dec 22	Dec 23	Dec 24	Dec 25	Dec 26	Dec 27	Dec 28	Dec 29	Dec 30	Dec 31	Jan 1	Jan 2
Maximum noise level dB	85	103	85	99	110	105	110	Closed	Closed	85	90	99	95	109	70	88

Research

8 Plan an investigation to find out how the tightness of the drum skin affects the volume and pitch of the note it makes. If you can, carry out your investigation.

Presentation

9 Create a presentation to show how a musical instrument makes a sound. Use photographs and diagrams in your presentation. If you can, include recordings of the instrument being played.

Revision checklist

I know:

- Sound is a form of energy. It travels as a longitudinal wave in solids, liquids and gases. A guitar produces tiny waves in the air when the string bumps against air particles. These tiny to-and-fro movements create pressure waves which move through the air. We hear these as sound.

- Frequency is the number of complete waves that arrive at a point in a second. High-pitched notes have a high frequency but bass notes have a low frequency. The pitch of the note made by a plucked string depends on:
  - length – longer strings give deeper notes
  - thickness – thicker strings tend to give deeper notes
  - tension – tight strings give higher-pitched notes.

- Sound can be represented by transverse wave diagrams. The wavelength is the distance between one crest and the next. The amplitude is the height of the wave.

- The volume of sound is measured in decibels. A library is about 20 dB. A jet plane taking off is about 130 dB. Very loud sounds damage the ear. Local authorities often measure sound levels to make sure they do not get too loud.

- Sound waves can be reflected from solid objects. This reflection is called an echo. Echo sounding equipment uses the time difference between the sound and its echo to work out distances.

- Sound does not travel in a vacuum. It moves at different speeds through solids, liquids and gases. Earthquakes produce shock waves which can be detected by seismometers.

36.1 Using energy

➡ What do we use energy for?

This looks tough! The athlete is using lots of energy to move the plane. We use energy to complete everyday tasks such as getting to and from school and playing sport.

Energy exists in different forms. The main types of energy are **movement energy** and **stored energy**. Food has stored energy. Our bodies **transfer** the energy from food and use it to move around, grow and repair. Any energy that isn't needed straight away is stored as **fat**.

Heat is often given out when energy is transferred. This is why we get hot when we exercise.

moving the body or other things

keeping the heart beating

repairing damaged parts of the body

growing taller

spare energy stored as fat

Questions

1 List all of the energy transfers your body has made today.

2 Why do you think you get hungry after a PE lesson?

3 Look at the photograph. Do you think that the athlete needs to eat more or less food than you? Why?

4 What have you done today that needed the most energy?

5 To lose weight you can either eat less food or do more exercise. Explain why either of these would work.

Keywords

movement energy

stored energy

transfer

fat

36.2 Keeping food warm

> **How can we keep food warm?**

Most take-away food is hot, so you need to keep it warm until you are ready to eat it. You have to stop heat passing out through the packaging of the food. Materials which slow down the movement of heat are called **insulators**. Plastic is a good insulator. Many insulators, such as **polystyrene** and cardboard, have small spaces within them which trap air. Air is a very good insulator.

Some materials allow heat to pass easily through them. These materials are called **conductors**. **Metals** are good conductors of heat.

Questions

1 List some materials used to package take-away food.
2 Which of these materials are insulators?
3 How do pizza delivery firms keep their pizza warm for customers?
4 Design a range of containers for baked potatoes, fish and chips and burgers.
5 Sort the materials in your list from question 1 into a table with these headings: 'Can rot away', 'Cannot rot away', 'Recyclable' and 'Non-recyclable'. Remember that the same packaging may be written under more than one heading.

Keywords

insulators
polystyrene
conductors
metals

36.3 Solar kettles

➡️ **How do we measure energy?**

These **solar kettles** make the world's most environmentally-friendly cuppa! Sunlight energy reflects from the huge curved mirrors onto the bottom of the kettle. The energy boils the water in the kettle.

How much **energy** does it need to warm something up? It depends on:

● how hot you want to get something
● how much of it you want to warm up
● what it is made from.

Energy is measured in **joules**. It takes 4.2 joules to raise water temperature by 1°C. Metals are much easier to warm up. The same amount of energy could raise the temperature of an equal mass of aluminium by over 4°C.

Monks in Drepang Monastery, Tibet, like a nice bowl of yak stew with their tea. This time the heat is provided by burning wood and charcoal in giant ovens. When you're cooking for nearly 1000 monks the solar kettles would be just too slow!

Questions

1 How can you tell sunlight contains energy?

2 What does the energy in the sunlight do to the water in the solar kettle?

3 List three things that control how much energy you need to add to something to warm it up.

4 What units is energy measured in?

5 Why are solar cookers not used to boil soup for the monks at Drepang monastery?

Keywords

solar kettles

energy

joules

Hot stuff

36.4 Up, up and away!

 How do hot air balloons work?

Hot air **balloons** are becoming increasingly popular. Many people are given a balloon ride as a birthday or Christmas present. The balloons come in all shapes and sizes but are all filled with the same thing – hot air.

A hot air balloon flies because hot air rises. A balloon pilot makes the balloon go up by increasing the **temperature** of the air inside the balloon. The warmer air floats upwards, carrying the balloon with it. To make the balloon go down the pilot just releases hot air from the balloon. Steering is more difficult – the wind pushes the balloon along in whichever direction it is going!

You can see warm air rising from fires and even candles. The smoke is carried upwards in the stream of hot air.

Questions

1 Which force pulls the balloon towards the ground?
2 Name the force that makes the balloon rise.
3 What must a pilot do to make the hot air balloon go higher?
4 What makes the balloon travel from one place to another?
5 What would happen to the balloon if the uplift and gravity forces were the same?

Keywords

balloon

temperature

36 Data response: Keeping warm

Insulation cuts the energy entering and leaving your house. This keeps you warmer in the winter and cooler in the summer. But which insulation is best?

Energy lost per square metre on a cold winter's day in the UK

Barrier	Energy lost (joules)
Single layer of brick, no plaster	36
Double layer of brick with plaster	27
Cavity wall with plaster	17
Concrete wall (100 mm thick)	40
Concrete wall (150 mm thick)	36
Single glazed window	57
Double glazed window	28

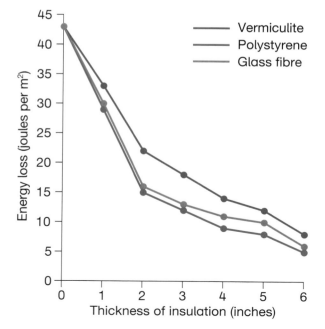

Cost of insulation changes and value of energy savings

Type of insulation	Cost of fitting (£)	Energy saved per year (£)
Cavity wall insulation	350	100
Adding loft insulation	200	25
Insulating hot water tank	10	12.50
Draught-proofing doors	50	12.50
Double glazing	1500	50

1 How much energy is lost by a concrete wall of 100 mm?

2 Which barrier loses 36 joules per square metre?

3 Which barrier loses the most energy?

4 Which is the cheapest sort of insulation?

5 Draw a chart to show the energy loss from the barriers in the first table.

6 Which type of insulation gives the best result at 4 cm deep?

7 How many years would it take to get back the cost of cavity wall insulation?

Research

8 What is the best shape for a solar reflector for a kettle? Plan an investigation to find out. Clue – you could use aluminium foil to give different shaped mirrors.

Presentation

9 Prepare a five-minute radio programme telling people how to cut their fuel bills. Include advice about loft insulation, cavity wall insulation, draft proofing and double glazing.

Revision checklist

I know:

- Energy exists in different forms. Energy can be transferred from one form to another.
- The main uses of heat energy are generating electricity, heating and cooking.
- Heat energy flows from a hot to a cooler body. Temperature is measured in °C. Energy is measured in joules. The energy to change the temperature of a body depends on its mass, the material it is made from, and the size of the temperature change.
- Heat can change the state of a substance without changing its temperature (ice to water, water to steam).
- Light from the Sun is reflected to a focus by a curved mirror. When light is absorbed by a surface, light energy is transferred to heat energy.
- Hot air rises and is replaced by colder air. This is used in hot air balloons to lift the basket.
- Metals are good conductors of heat. Trapped air and plastics are good insulators. Insulation reduces heat loss.

37.1 Making electricity

How do generators work?

Introducing Personal PowerStation! You can get a radio or a torch that never need batteries. These devices have a tiny generator in them. You turn the handle to generate electricity and charge the built-in batteries. But how much winding do you need to do?

How long does the charge last?

Winding time	Torch	Radio
10	300	600
20	600	1200
30	900	1800

All times in minutes.

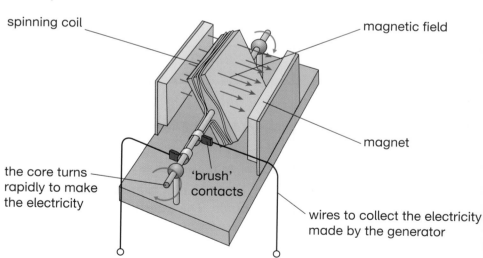

The PowerStation works in the same way as all **generators**. When a wire moves in a **magnetic field**, electricity starts to flow along the wire. Generators usually **spin** a **magnet** inside a **coil** of wire. To get more electricity out you can:

- spin the magnet more quickly
- use a stronger magnet
- use more coils of wire.

spinning coil

magnetic field

the core turns rapidly to make the electricity

'brush' contacts

magnet

wires to collect the electricity made by the generator

Questions

1 Give one advantage of the PowerStation compared with ordinary batteries.

2 How long do you need to wind for 600 minutes of radio reception?

3 How long would the torch last after 60 minutes winding?

4 List three ways to increase the electricity made by a generator.

5 Draw a design for a generator turned by a hamster wheel.

Keywords

generator
magnetic field
spin
magnet
coil

Nuclear power

37.2 Hot atoms

How do nuclear power stations work?

Atoms are the tiny building blocks that link together to make the air we breathe, the food we eat and even this book. There are about 100 different types of atom. It is the way they link together that makes all the different things you can see.

Most atoms never change. They are a bit like super-hard snooker balls. But some split up into smaller atoms. These are **radioactive** atoms. The power station in the photograph uses radioactive **uranium** atoms. They give out heat when they break apart. This heat boils water to make steam. The steam turns giant **turbines** which spin **generators** to make electricity.

Most of the power station buildings are there to control this reaction. It only happens in the **core**. A lead and concrete shield keeps the dangerous uranium away from living things.

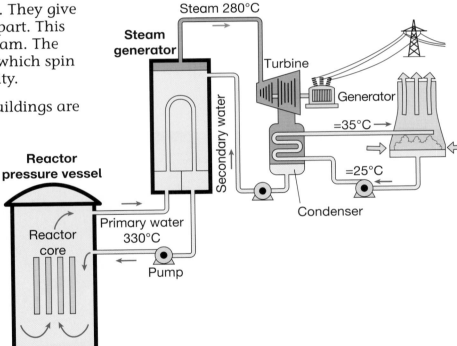

Questions

1 Write a sentence that uses the word atom.
2 What is special about radioactive atoms?
3 What is the radioactive metal that produces heat in a nuclear power station?
4 What makes the generators spin?
5 Draw a flow chart to show how uranium makes electricity.

Keywords

atom

radioactive

uranium

turbine

generator

core

37.3 Dangerous waste

 What is nuclear waste?

Nuclear power plants don't just produce electricity. They also produce **radioactive waste**. This will stay dangerous for many thousands of years and must be kept away from people until it is safe. You can see the sign for radiation hazard on the drums in the photo.

Sometimes the radioactive waste must be moved from power stations to a safe **storage** place. Special trains carry strong containers of the waste. The photograph shows a test on one of these containers. Even when a train crashes into it at full speed it must not break!

Plutonium is a waste metal produced by the decay of uranium. It is the metal used to make **atomic bombs**. Many people are worried that countries with nuclear power stations could collect enough plutonium to make their own atomic bomb.

Questions

1 What is radioactive waste?

2 For how long is radioactive waste stored?

3 What is plutonium?

4 What is plutonium used to make?

5 Why is radioactive waste moved from power stations?

Keywords

radioactive waste

storage

plutonium

atomic bomb

37.4 'Nuclear power? No thanks!'

 Can we make nuclear power completely safe?

*We need **nuclear power**. Coal, gas and oil are running out and when we burn them they worsen **global warming**. We need energy and the only way we can get it is through nuclear power. We have no choice. The Green Party may be happy to go back to the Middle Ages with everyone living on farms and with no electricity – but I'm not!*

*Nuclear power is expensive and dangerous. It produces nuclear waste which will never be safe. Nuclear power stations are also unreliable – look at the accidents! And imagine a terrorist attack on a nuclear power station! It's not even renewable – we will run out of **uranium** to use in these power stations in the next hundred years anyway! We should build wind turbines and work on saving energy… and say 'no thanks' to nuclear!*

The UK Atomic Energy Authority (**UKAEA**) was set up by the government in 1954. It has worked to develop nuclear power stations and weapons. Nowadays its main work is to clean up the nuclear power stations as they near the end of their useful lives. The UKAEA reports to the government to make sure that Britain has a safe nuclear industry.

Questions

1 Give two benefits of nuclear power.
2 Give two problems with nuclear power.
3 What do you think is the biggest problem with nuclear power? Why?
4 What does the UKAEA do?
5 Design a solar-powered still to separate fresh water from sea water.

Keywords

nuclear power
global warming
uranium
UKAEA

37 Data response: Nuclear power in Europe

The number of working nuclear power stations in European countries

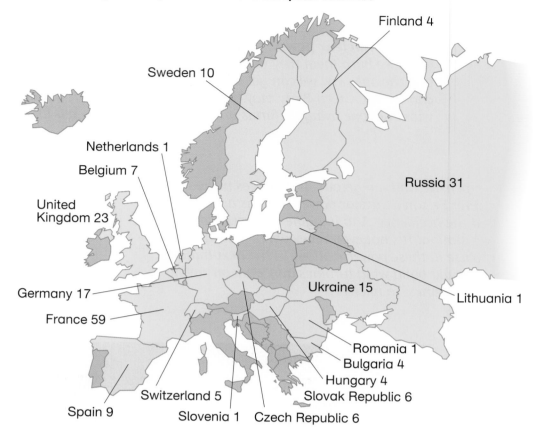

Different sources of energy used for electricity generation in Europe (2003/2004)

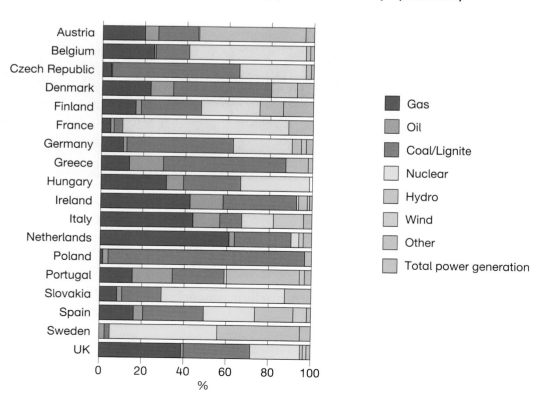

Nuclear power

1 How many nuclear reactors are there in Germany?

2 Which country in Europe has the most nuclear reactors?

3 Which country gets most of its electricity from gas-fired power stations?

4 Which countries have no working power stations?

5 Which country gets most of its electricity from nuclear power?

6 Draw a bar chart to show how many working power stations are present in the UK, France, Germany, Sweden and Spain.

Research

7 Prepare a survey to find out what the people think about nuclear power. Collect at least 30 sets of results and include males and females in your sample.

Once you have the data, prepare a report that includes graphs and charts to show what people think.

Presentation

8 Should we use nuclear power to generate electricity? Prepare a presentation that shows both sides of this argument. Make sure you include some facts and figures in the presentation as well as opinions.

Revision checklist

I know:

- Moving a wire in a magnetic field makes electricity. Generators use coils of wires and large powerful magnets. The amount of electricity generated can be increased by spinning the magnet faster or using a stronger magnet or more coils of wire. Generators in power stations use electromagnets.

- In a nuclear power station, the breakdown of radioactive uranium makes heat to boil water. The steam turns turbines which turn generators to make electricity. Uranium is a non-renewable resource.

- Power stations produce radioactive waste materials in the core. They are isolated from the rest of the power station by lead and concrete shields.

- A nuclear power station produces harmful radioactive waste. Plutonium is a waste product from nuclear power. It can be used to make nuclear bombs.

- A government agency called the UK Atomic Energy Authority (UKAEA) is responsible for nuclear safety.

- The risks of nuclear power include nuclear waste, the possibility of explosions or terrorist damage and the chance that nuclear power stations can be used to make atomic weapons. The benefit of nuclear power is that it does not produce as much carbon dioxide as a coal-fired power station.

38.1 Christmas lights

 What is the electromagnetic spectrum?

Christmas lights outside a house in Norfolk… every colour of the **spectrum**!

The difference between red and blue light is the **wavelength**. Red lights have a longer wavelength than blue but they are all part of the spectrum of visible light. White light is a mixture of all of the colours in the spectrum. We can see the complete spectrum in a rainbow or in light bent by a prism of glass: Red, Orange, Yellow, Green, Blue, Indigo, Violet. A good mnemonic to remember this is: Richard Of York Gave Battle In Vain.

The visible spectrum is only a part of the wider **electromagnetic spectrum**. This runs all the way from radio waves to gamma rays.

Laser light is intense light of one wavelength. High-power lasers are used for displays and even for cutting metals. Low-power lasers are used to read compact discs.

Electromagnetic spectrum

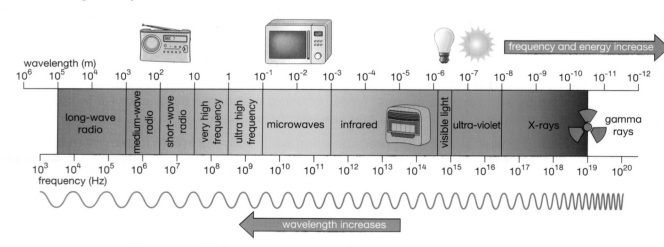

Questions

1 Starting with red, write out the order of coloured lights in the spectrum.

2 List three uses of lasers.

3 Which has more energy – gamma rays or infrared?

4 How can you split white light up into its different colours?

5 What is the electromagnetic spectrum?

Keywords

spectrum

wavelength

electromagnetic spectrum

laser

Full spectrum

38.2 Infrared control

> **What do we use infrared radiation for?**

When a burglar walks through the **infrared rays** given out by a burglar alarm, the alarm goes off.

Infrared is used at home every day. TV and stereo remote controls use invisible **infrared radiation** to carry signals from the handset to the television. Electric cookers have hot-plates. They glow and give out red light. They also give out infrared rays. The infrared radiation, not the red light, heats up the food. Infrared radiation can therefore burn.

When you want to take photographs at night, you use a flash with the camera to make sure that there is enough light. Security cameras cannot use flash photography because burglars would know the cameras were there! Instead, security cameras use infrared rays to produce a good picture.

Questions

1 How does a burglar set off a burglar alarm?
2 Name three things in the home that use infrared rays.
3 Look at the two photographs. Which one was taken using an infrared camera?
4 Can a mirror reflect infrared light? Plan an investigation to find out.

Keywords

infrared rays

infrared radiation

38.3 Radios and cookers

What do we use radiowaves and microwaves for?

Full spectrum

The **aerial** on your radio picks up waves that are sent from the **transmitter** at the radio station. This makes a tiny electric current flow in the aerial. Electronic circuits in the radio convert these signals into sounds.

Radio waves are sent out at different frequency bands. Most radio stations transmit at **very high frequencies (VHF)**. These waves can only carry sound. Television stations transmit at **ultra high frequency (UHF)**. UHF signals can carry sound and pictures.

A **microwave** is a type of radiation with an even higher frequency. Modern communication devices like mobile phones use microwaves. You have probably seen microwave antennae on buildings around towns and cities. The dishes on the Telecom Tower in London carry millions of phonecalls every second.

Microwaves are also used in cookers. They pass through the food in the oven, warming it up from the inside very quickly. Special shielding in the oven stops the microwaves from leaking out and heating up your insides!

Questions

1 How does a radio receive sound?
2 At what frequency do televisions receive sound and pictures?
3 What type of waves do mobile phones receive?
4 How does a microwave oven cook food?
5 Why do microwave ovens switch off automatically when you open the door?

Keywords

aerial

transmitter

very high frequencies (VHF)

ultra high frequency (UHF)

microwave

38.4 Killer phones?

Are mobile phones safe?

Mobile phones use **microwave radiation**. The sounds and texts are coded then transmitted from phone to mast to phone by microwaves. Some people are concerned that these microwaves could cause changes in the brain that lead to **cancer**. But what does the **evidence** say?

*Microwaves do cause very slight warming of cells. They have shown this in the lab – I'll feel safer not taking the **risk**!*

There is no evidence at all linking mobile phones and brain cancer. This is just another health scare.

In a BBC survey 40% of people said they would continue to use mobile phones even if it was proved they did cause cancer! People just can't live without them anyway!

The amount of radiation used by mobile phones is tiny. And I only use my phone a few times a day so I'm not worried. Not sure I'd want to live next to a mobile phone mast though!

The evidence so far shows no connection between mobile phones and cancer. But it may be wise to be careful. It is difficult to prove that mobile phones are safe. All we can say is we have no evidence that they are dangerous – yet.

Questions

1. What sort of radiation do mobile phones use?
2. What does a mobile phone mast do?
3. Do you have a mobile phone?
4. Roughly how many minutes do you use your mobile every day?
5. Give three pieces of advice to reduce the risk of brain cancer from using your mobile phone.

Keywords

microwave radiation

risk

cancer

evidence

38 Data response: Phone bills

Phone companies have so many different ways to take your money! What package is best for you? It's not always easy to decide.

1 First **choose your phone** – sometimes they are free, sometimes you have to pay extra.

Nokia N70

Tariff	Cost
100+	£15.99
200+	£15.99
250+	£15.99
400	FREE
600	FREE
Leisure	£21.99
Max	FREE

Motorola V3x

Tariff	Cost
100+	£11.99
200+	£11.99
250+	FREE
400	FREE
600	FREE
Leisure	£19.99
Max	FREE

LG P7200

Tariff	Cost
100+	£21.99
200+	£21.99
250+	£21.99
400	FREE
600	FREE
Leisure	£29.99
Max	FREE

Samsung D600

Tariff	Cost
100+	£15.99
200+	£15.99
250+	£15.99
400	FREE
600	FREE
Leisure	£21.99
Max	FREE

2 Then **choose your tariff**. How many free minutes a month do you want?

[1] first nine months free if you sign up for two years

[2] free calls and texts only available offpeak

Tariff	Line rental (£)	Free minutes	Free texts
100+	12.50	200	200
200+	15.00	400	200
250+	35.00[1]	500	200
400	45.00	800	200
600	60.00	800	200
Leisure[2]	10.00	1000	200
Max	75.00	2000	200

3 Remember, you still have to **pay for the calls**. Different tariffs charge different amounts. When will you use your mobile phone?

Cost of calls in pence per minute

Tariffs	Calls to UK landlines		Calls to mobiles on on same network		Calls to mobiles other networks		Text messages	
	Peak	Offpeak	Peak	Offpeak	Peak	Offpeak	Peak	Offpeak
100+ 200+	15	10	15	10	45	40	14	10
250+ 400 600	10	10	10	10	40	40	12	10
Leisure	30	2	30	2	45	30	12	12
Max	4	2	3	2	30	30	12	12

Data response

1 How much does it cost to buy a Samsung D600 on the 250+ tariff?

2 Which phone is free on the 250+ tariff?

3 How many free minutes do you get with a 400 tariff?

4 How much do offpeak minutes cost to landlines on the leisure tariff?

5 Which tariff has the most expensive text messages?

6 I've made 340 minutes of calls on my 200+ tariff this month. All of them were in the day to a UK landline. How much will my bill be for these calls?

7 Recommend a tariff for each of the following people.

I use my phone for business. I often get up to 2500 minutes a month – mainly during the day.

I use my phone mainly during the evenings and weekends when I'm not at college. I send quite a lot of texts but still get up to about 400 minutes of calls a month.

I've only really got the phone for emergencies. My mother is quite old and I like to think she can get hold of me anytime of the day or night. Last month I used just 20 minutes all month.

Research

8 How strong are infrared remotes for televisions and stereos? Plan an investigation to find out how close you have to be and how carefully you have to aim a remote control for it to work.

Presentation

9 Prepare a chart or presentation to show the different parts of the electromagnetic spectrum. Include photographs and text to show how the different types of rays can be used – and any dangers.

Revision checklist

I know:

- Visible light is part of a group of waves called the electromagnetic spectrum. The visible spectrum runs **R**ed, **O**range, **Y**ellow, **G**reen, **B**lue, **I**ndigo, **V**iolet. A good way to remember this is **R**ichard **O**f **Y**ork **G**ave **B**attle **I**n **V**ain. A rainbow is a naturally occurring visible spectrum.

- A laser produces a narrow intense beam of light. Lasers are used to read CDs, for light shows, as pointers and as cutting tools.

- Infrared light is useful for:
  - remote controls
  - night photography
  - burglar alarms
  - heating things, for example in fires, toasters, grills.

- Microwaves heat materials containing particles that the microwave radiation can vibrate. Microwaves are used in cookers, mobile phones and radar telephone links. Some people worry that microwave radiation used for mobile phones could have long-term harmful effects on our brains.

- Radiowaves produce electrical signals in metal aerials. Electronic circuits amplify these tiny signals to make sounds and pictures. Radiowaves are used for radio, mobile telephones and wireless links for laptop computers.

- Wireless technology is used for global communications. Its main advantage is that we do not need to lay expensive wires and cables over long distances. Cables can also break, cutting off the signal. Satellites orbiting the Earth can send radio signals all around the planet.

39.1 Looking inside

 Why do doctors use X-rays?

Jimmy's mother said not to put the key in his mouth! Now he'll just have to hope it comes out by itself – or he'll have to have an operation!

Doctors use **X-rays** to look inside their patients' bodies – perhaps for broken bones, diseased lungs or objects that were swallowed by mistake. X-rays are shone through the body onto special photographic film. Metal objects and heavy body parts like bone block the X-rays. These areas show up as white when the film is developed.

X-rays help doctors to diagnose what is wrong with a patient. When doctors know the **diagnosis**, they can suggest a way to treat the disease.

But X-rays are not risk-free. They carry a lot of **energy** and this can sometimes damage the body. To reduce the risk of damage doctors will only ask for an X-ray when they need the information it gives to help with the diagnosis and no other method will work.

People who work with X-rays every day must take care to stop the harmful rays from damaging their bodies. They often switch on the X-ray machine from behind a special **lead** screen.

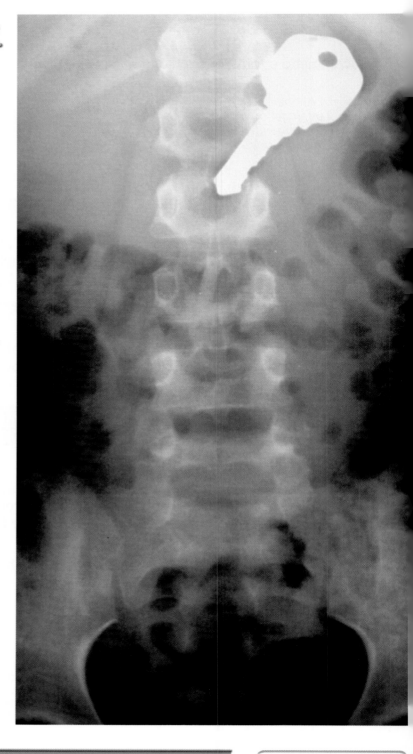

Medical rays

Questions

1 What does the word 'diagnosis' mean?

2 Why is a diagnosis essential before treatment begins?

3 Give three uses of X-rays.

4 What is the main disadvantage of X-rays?

5 How do people who work with X-rays every day protect themselves from radiation?

Keywords

X-rays

diagnosis

energy

lead

39.2 Suntans

What is ultraviolet light?

Ultraviolet light is part of the **electromagnetic spectrum**. It has a shorter wavelength and gives out more energy than visible light. Ultraviolet radiation gives us a suntan. Doctors sometimes suggest a course of UV light because it helps the skin to make some vitamins and can clear up some skin problems.

But if people spend too much time in the Sun, they get sunburn. The skin goes red and peels. Even more exposure to ultraviolet radiation can cause skin **cancer**.

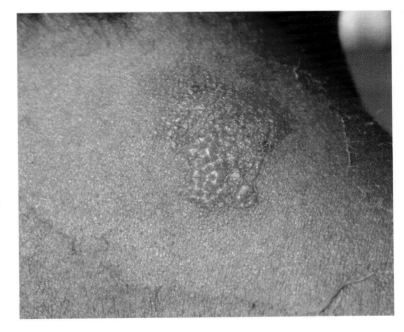

Suntan cream blocks UV light.
The **Sun Protection Factor (SPF)** tells you how much UV is screened out. For very sunny countries you need an SPF of 30, for countries that are less sunny, an SPF of 10 may be enough. People with pale skin need to use a higher SPF.

Australia has high rates of skin cancer. To give people advice about how to protect themselves the government launched the Slip, slop, slap! campaign.

Suncreams and SPF

Brand	SPF	Suitable for:
SurfBronzer	8	People who tan easily and do not burn. Medium sunlight exposure.
GoldenTan	15	People with pale skins who burn in the sun. Protects against medium sunlight.
SuperBronze	35	People of all skin types spending a lot of time outside in very sunny countries or while climbing mountains.

Slip on a shirt, slop on sunscreen and slap on a hat

Questions

1 Give two medical uses of UV radiation.
2 Give two reasons why too much sun is bad for you.
3 What is a Sun Protection Factor?
4 Give three ways you can protect yourself against skin cancer caused by UV light.
5 Which of the sun creams in the table is most suitable for a trip across the Sahara?

Keywords

ultraviolet (UV)

electromagnetic spectrum

cancer

Sun Protection Factor (SPF)

39.3 Kill that cancer!

⇨ **How is radiation used to treat cancer?**

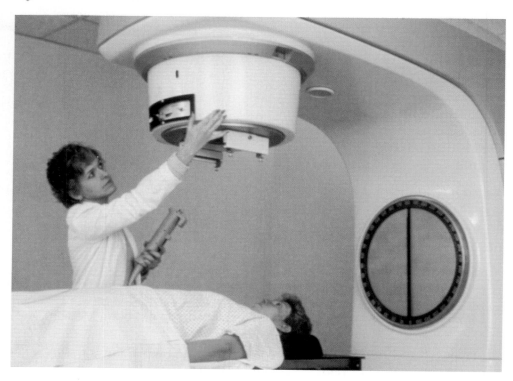

Medical rays

Radiation can cause **cancer** – but can also cure it. A group of cancer cells is called a **tumour**. Doses of gamma rays are fired at the cancerous tumour until it is destroyed. Treating cancer with radiation is called **radiotherapy**. The dose and type of radiation has to be carefully controlled. Too little radiation will not kill the tumour but too much will make the patient even more ill. People often suffer from serious **side-effects** with radiotherapy.

Gamma rays are very high energy waves. They pass through the body like X-rays. Using special cameras linked to computers, gamma rays can give us a picture of inside the body. The risks with **gamma cameras** are similar to those with X-rays so they are only used when absolutely necessary.

Some tests use chemicals that give out gamma rays. The patient swallows the chemicals and they collect in certain parts of the body which then show up well on a gamma camera.

Questions

1 What does the word 'tumour' mean?

2 How is radiation used to treat cancer?

3 Why is it important to get the dose and type of radiation correct in radiotherapy?

4 Why do we not use gamma cameras every day?

5 Give two body parts that can be pictured with gamma cameras.

Keywords

radiation

cancer

tumour

radiotherapy

side-effect

gamma rays

gamma camera

39.4 Background radiation

What is background radiation?

The radiation that is around us all the time is called **background radiation**. It comes out of the ground from some types of rock. The rocks in Cornwall and Devon give out more radiation than other parts of the country. But that doesn't worry the people at this seaside cafe in Cornwall. Our food and drink is **radioactive** and so is the air we breathe! Every day, radiation from space hits the Earth. We use a device called a **Geiger counter** to measure radiation.

Background radiation is natural and is so low that it probably does little harm. The problems really begin when the level of radiation in the environment goes up. This can be caused by human activity such as the testing of nuclear weapons or explosions at nuclear power stations like Chernobyl.

No radiation level is completely safe. Even the lowest levels may do some harm – but how big is this **risk**? One way to display the risk is to link it with something people understand – like cigarette smoking.

Radioactive risks equal to smoking cigarettes

Radiation dose	Cigarette equivalent (lifetime)
Chest X-ray	9
Skull X-ray	44
Bone scan	1300
Background radiation	450

Questions

1 What is background radiation?

2 Where does background radiation come from?

3 What do we use to measure radiation?

4 What is the cigarette equivalent of one chest X-ray?

5 If chest X-rays have a risk, why do people have them?

Keywords

background radiation

radioactive

Geiger counter

risk

39 Data response: Safe sunbathing

Site of skin cancers

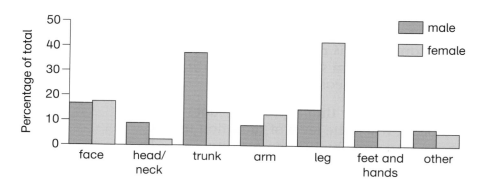

Legend: ■ male ■ female

Y-axis: Percentage of total (0, 10, 20, 30, 40, 50)

X-axis: face, head/neck, trunk, arm, leg, feet and hands, other

Holidays since 1966

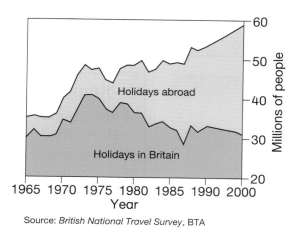

Holidays abroad

Holidays in Britain

Y-axis: Millions of people (20, 30, 40, 50, 60)

X-axis: Year (1965, 1970, 1975, 1980, 1985, 1990, 2000)

Source: *British National Travel Survey*, BTA

Rate of skin cancer cases in the UK per 100 000 people

Year	Males	Females
1981	3.3	5.5
1982	3.4	5.9
1983	3.7	6.3
1984	3.7	6.2
1985	4.8	7.9
1986	4.9	7.7
1987	5.4	8.4
1988	6.5	9.2
1989	5.9	8.6
1990	6.2	7.9
1991	6.1	7.9
1992	6.6	8.6
1993	7.6	9.7
1994	7.5	9.7
1995	7.5	10.0
1996	7.6	9.6
1997	8.1	9.8
1998	8.6	10.0
1999	8.6	9.9
2000	9.7	11.2
2001	10.2	11.8

1 Is the rate of skin cancer going up or down?

2 What year did the rate of skin cancer in males go above 5 per 100 000 people?

3 What was the rate of skin cancer in females in 1988?

4 Which part of the body is most likely to suffer from skin cancer in females?

5 Which part of the body is most likely to suffer from skin cancer in males?

6 Suggest one reason for this difference in males and females.

7 Someone has suggested that people going on foreign holidays to sunny countries has caused an increase in skin cancer. Find one piece of evidence on these pages that supports this idea.

Research

8 What is the background radiation in your area? Use the internet to try to find out the level of background radiation where you live.

Presentation

9 Design a poster to show people how to make sure they get a healthy-looking tan, not painful red sunburn. The poster should be suitable for display at seaside resorts and even on beaches so needs to be colourful.

Revision checklist

I know:

- Doctors diagnose an illness by looking at symptoms. Looking inside the body can help a doctor to reach a diagnosis. Looking inside the body has risks – either from surgery or some of the machines that use radiation.

- Doctors use UV radiation to treat skin conditions. Too much UV radiation causes sunburn and even skin cancer. The risks of UV light can be reduced by using sun cream, covering up, wearing a hat and avoiding the strong midday sun.

- Bone absorbs X-rays and produces shadow pictures on special films. X-rays carry a lot of energy and exposure to them is dangerous. Doctors have to balance the benefits of X-rays against the risks to the patient.

- Gamma radiation is the most penetrating type of electromagnetic radiation. It can be detected by a gamma camera. A computer linked to the camera can make pictures that are visible on a screen. Exposure to gamma rays is very dangerous.

- UV radiation, X-rays and gamma rays are part of the electromagnetic spectrum. UV radiation, X-rays and gamma rays can damage living cells.

- Some radiation is natural, and this is called background radiation. Although it is natural it is not harmless.

adaptation	a feature of a living organism that helps it to survive, e.g. the zebra's stripes are an adaptation that makes it difficult to see in the wild and so protects it from lions
additives	chemicals added to foods to improve the flavour or appearance or shelflife
aerial	the part of a radio or television that picks up the signal in the air
alkali	a substance which makes a solution that turns red litmus paper blue
amplitude	the difference between the highest and lowest points on a wave, the larger the amplitude of a sound wave the louder the sound
antibodies	chemicals produced by cells called B lymphocytes which attack invading microorganisms
antiobiotics	chemicals produced by a living thing like a fungus or bacterium that can kill bacteria
antioxidants	chemicals which delay the oxidation of other chemicals; they are important in paints, plastics and rubbers where they slow down degradation of the material; Vitamin C is an antioxidant in the body
artificial sweetener	a chemical other than sugar added to food to make it taste sweet
aspartame	a common artificial sweetener
asteroids	lumps of rock orbiting the Sun, too small to be called a planet
atmosphere	the mixture of gases we call the air; the atmosphere is about 80% nitrogen and 20% oxygen with other gases making up less than 1%
atom	the smallest part of an element; atoms consist of negatively-charged electrons flying around a positively-charged nucleus
atomic bomb	a bomb that produces an explosion from atomic reactions
background radiation	very low level radiation from space and rocks that is around us all the time
bacteria	microscopic single-celled living things that have no nucleus
binocular	having two eyepieces or two eyes, e.g. binocular vision uses two eyes to judge distances
biodegradable	a substance which can be broken down by biological action in the environment
breeds	types of animals that belong to the same species, e.g. poodles and alsatians are breeds of dog
cadmium	a metal used in mobile phones
cancer	a dangerous illness caused by radiation, smoking and some types of chemicals; cancer cells grow out of control to make lumps of cells, they can also invade normal healthy areas of the body
carbon dioxide	a gas containing only carbon and oxygen; its chemical formula is CO_2
carbon monoxide	a poisonous gas containing only carbon and oxygen
carnivores	an animal that eats other animals
catalyst	a chemical that speeds up a reaction but is not changed by it or used up by the reaction
centrifuging	spinning something around very fast to separate solids from a liquid
charcoal	charcoal forms when wood is heated without air; it is a black substance that is mostly carbon; it can burn with a very hot flame; it can also be used for drawing on paper
chemical reaction	a change that occurs when a number of substances react together to produce new substances

chromatogram	the pattern produced when a mixture of soluble substances is separated by chromatography
chromatography	the science of producing chromatograms
chromosomes	threadlike structures in cells which contain genetic material
clones	two living thing are clones if they have exactly the same genes
coil	a spiral, often made of wire; coils are often used in electrical circuits to magnetise metal objects
combustion	combustion is the reaction between a fuel and oxygen to form carbon dioxide and water, and releases energy as light and heat
comet	a small body that moves through space and reflects light; comets often show a tail caused by particles of dust and ice that trail behind them as they move
condense	a gas condenses when it changes into a liquid
conductors	a substance that will let heat or electricity pass through it; a bar of copper is a good example of a conductor
consumption	the amount that someone or a country uses up
continental drift	the movenment of giant tectonic plates across the surface of the Earth
core	the middle of something
cornea	the clear layer at the front of the eye; the cornea helps to focus the light going into the eyeball
cradle to grave	a cradle to grave analysis of a product looks at every stage of its life from the original materials used to make it through to what happens whjen it is finally disposed of
crater	a roughly circular dip in the ground created by the impact of a meteorite
crude oil	oil extracted from the ground before it has been refined
crust	the solid surface of rock covering the Earth
cuttings	parts of a plant that can under certain circumstances grow into a new plant
cystic fibrosis	a genetic illness that affects the lungs and digestive system
debris	rubbish
decant	to pour the liquid off the top of a solid to leave the solid behind
decibel	the unit of loudness
deflect	to turn aside
diagnosis	to recognise a particular disease
dialysis	a process used to clean blood; blood is filtered by passing it over a partially permeable membrane; dissolved substances diffuse from the blood through the membrane into a fluid on the other side and are removed
diesel	a fuel used in cars and larger road vehicles
dissolve	when a solid mixes in with a liquid so that it cannot be seen
distillation	scientists use distillation to boil off a liquid from a mixture and then cool the vapours to produce a purer liquid
DNA	the molecule that carries the genetic information in animals and higher plants; DNA is short for DeoxyriboNucleic Acid
dormant	a plant or seed is dormant if it is still alive but fails to grow even though the correct conditions for growth are available

E300	the standard code number for vitamin C used in European food labels
earthquake	a sudden movement of the Earth's crust in an area
echo	a sound bouncing back from a solid object like a wall or a cliff
effector	a part of the body that produces an effect, for example a muscle
electromagnetic spectrum	the whole range of electromagnetic waves, extending from radio waves to gamma rays
emulsifiers	a chemical which can help to break fats up into small globules so that they do not settle out of suspension
energy	energy is the ability of a system to do something (work); we detect energy by the effect it has on the things around us – heating them up, moving them, etc.
environment	all the things around us
enzyme	special proteins found in living organisms that speed up the rate of a chemical reaction
erupt	a volcano erupts when steam, gases or lava is forced out of it by pressure from within the Earth
evaporate	to dry up, usually below the boiling point; even cold water can evaporate on a windy day
evidence	evidence includes all the results and data collected from investigations; people should agree about evidence even if they disagree about what a piece of evidence means
extinct	a species is extinct when all members of the species have died
faeces	the solid waste from our gut
fertiliser	material added to the soil to make plants grow better, e.g. manure or chemical powders
field of view	the area you can see without moving your eyes
filter	to separate the solid particles from a liquid by passing the mixture through a fine mesh or paper
food chain	a simple diagram using arrows to show the feeding relationships between some plants and animals
food web	a diagram showing how all of the food chains in an area link together
fractional distillation	separating liquids with different boiling points; it is used in the oil industry to separate crude oil into different fractions
fractions	these are the simpler mixtures or single components obtained by fractionation
frequency	the number of vibrations per second; frequency is measured in Hertz
fuel	something that gives out energy, usually as light and heat, when it burns
fuel pellets	small burnable lumps made from rubbish
gamma camera	a camera that takes pictures using gamma rays not light
gamma rays	a type of very high energy electromagnetic radiation
geiger counter	a device to detect some types of radiation
generator	a device for converting energy of movement (kinetic energy) into electrical energy (current flow)
genes	the length of DNA that codes for a particular characteristic
genetic engineers	a range of technologies that allow scientists to manipulate individual genes – perhaps by moving them between different species

germination	the first stages of growth of a seed into a new plant
global warming	the gradual rise in average global temperature over the last century or so; it is almost certainly caused by human activity – mainly burning of fossil fuels like coal, gas and oil
granite	a very hard type of igneous rock
habitat	the area where an organism lives
herbivores	animals that eat plants
hydrochloric acid	an acid formed when hydrogen chloride gas (HCl) dissolves in water
hygienic	cleanliness
igneous	rocks formed from solidified molten magma
immune system	the parts of the body that protect against illnesses; the lymph glands are particularly important in the immune system
infections	illnesses caused by microorganisms
infrared radiation	radiation beyond the red end of the visible spectrum; efficient at transferring heat
infrared rays	a type of electromagnetic radiation just beyond the red end of visible light
insulators	substances that will not let energy pass through them easily; you can have insulators for heat, electricity or sound
iris	the coloured part of the eye
joules	a unit of energy; It takes 4.2 J to raise the temperature of 1 g of water by 1° C
lactic acid bacteria	bacteria that help to make yoghurt from milk
landfill	a place where rubbish is buried underground
landslide	when a large mass of land slides down a hill or mountainside
laser	a special kind of light beam that can carry a lot of energy and can be focussed very accurately; lasers are often used to judge the speed of moving objects or the distance to them
lava	molten rock thrown up by a volcano
lead	a dark grey soft metal
lens	a piece of glass that can change the direction of light rays
magma	molten rock inside the Earth
magnetic	an object that is magnetic is attracted by a magnet
magnetic field	an area where a magnetic force can be felt
mantle	the layer of semi-solid rock below the crust in the Earth
manure	the faeces of horses and cows – often mixed with straw and added to gardens to improve the soil
mass	mass describes the amount of something; it is measured in kilograms
metals	substances that are shiny when pure, can be beaten into sheets or drawn into wirers; metals usually have quite high melting points and conduct heat and electricity well
meteorite	a small asteroid entering the Earth's atmosphere
methane	a colourless, odourless gas that burns easily to give water and carbon dioxide
microorganisms	very small living things which you need a microscope to see; most are harmless, some are useful and some cause serious illnesses

microwave radiation	radiation with very short wavelengths that is used to cook food (in microwave ovens) and to carry signals (in mobile phones)
MMR	the combined vaccination for Mumps, Measles and Rubella
molten	something is molten if it has been heated to change it from a solid to a liquid
monocular	having only one eye or eyepiece; many microscopes and telescopes are monocular
monosodium glutamate	a chemical added to food that makes it taste stronger
moon	the Earth's natural satellite (also the largest!)
movement energy	energy a body has because it is moving, e.g. a moving car
Near Earth Object (NEO)	an asteroid that passes near the Earth
nerves	parts of the body that carry signals to and from the brain
neutral	a neutral solution has a pH of 7 and is neither acid nor alkaline
nitrogen	a non-reactive gas that makes up most of the atmosphere
non-biodegradable	living organisms cannot breakdown non-biodegradable objects; many plastics are non-biodegradable and so last for very, very long times in the environment
nucleus	the control centre of the cell – surrounded by a membrane that separates it from the rest of the cell
nulear power	using the heat from radioactive metals like uranium to produce electrical power
nutrients	another word for food groups like carbohydrates and fats; plants need certain chemicals from the soil and these are called mineral nutrients.
offspring	the young produced by reproduction
optic nerve	the nerve carrying impulses from the retina of the eye to the brain
oscilloscope	a device that displays a line on a screen showing reguar changes (oscillations) in something; an oscilloscope is often used to look at sound waves collected by a microphone
oxygen	a colourless gas with no smell that makes up about 20% of the air
particle	a very small part of something.
pasteurise	to heat milk up to just over 70°C for a few seconds and then cool again; this kills the harmful bacteria in the milk
petrol	a fuel made from oil and used to power road vehicles
pH	the range of levels of acidity or alkalinity; a pH of 7 is neutral; a pH below 7 is acid and the lower it goes the more acidic it becomes; a pH above 7 is alkaline
phosphorus	a non-metallic element that bursts into flame in air
photosynthesis	the production, in green plants, of sugar and oxygen from carbon dioxide and water using light as an external energy source
pitfall trap	a trap to catch ground-dwelling beetles and insects
planet	a large body moving around a star; we live on the planet Earth that is moving around a star we call the Sun
plutonium	a radioactive metal used to build atomic bombs
poisonous	poisonous substances kill you if you swallow them
polystyrene	a type of plastic
pooter	a device used to transfer small insects safely between containers in a laboratory

potassium	a soft metal that bursts into flame when it is dropped into cold water
predators	animals that hunt and kill other animals
pressure	the force acting on a surface divided by the area of the surface; it is measured in newtons per square metre (N/m^2)
prey	animals that are hunted by other animals
producer	an organism that makes organic material; green plants are sometimes called primary producers because they use energy from sunlight to make sugar
punnett square	a diagram to show the way genes will pass from parents to offspring
pupil	the clear space at the front of the eyeball that lets light into the eye
quadrat	frame or pointer used to mark out a sample of an area for more intensive study
radiation	energy that travels as light or electromagnetic waves; some sorts of nuclear radiation contains particles, e.g. beta radiation consists of a stream of high speed electrons
radioactive	material which gives out radiation
radioactive waste	waste produced by radioactive materials used at power stations, research centres and some hospitals
radiotherapy	using radiation to treat certain types of disease; radiotherapy is particularly useful in cancer treatment where carefully targeted radiation is used to kill the cancerous cells
RDA	the Recommended Daily Allowance of a foodstuff, perhaps a vitamin, is the amount dieticians recommend for a healthy diet
react	two chemicals react together to change each other into something new
reaction	a change in a group of chemicals where bonds between atoms are broken and remade to form new chemicals
reaction time	in biology, the time taken to respond to a stimulus; in chemistry, the time taken for a reaction to finish
receptor	nerve cells in the sense organs which detect stimuli, e.g. the eye has receptors for light
recover	to take back, often used to mean getting back the energy used to make something by burning it and using the heat to make electricity
recycle	turning wastes into useful materials
reflect	to bounce something back – usually light from a mirror or sound from a solid wall
reflex	an inborn stimulus-response pair that is usually to do with protecting the body from harm; reflexes are not usually under the control of the conscious brain
renewable	windpower, wave power and solar power are all examples of renewable sources of energy
resin	a type of chemical used in many glues and composite materials
response	something an animal does as a result of a stimulus, e.g. the pupil in the eye responds to bright light by getting smaller
retina	the layer of specialised nerve cells lining the inside of the eyeball that converts light into nerve impulses
reuse	to use something more than once, e.g. a milk bottle can be reused five or six times
risk	a risk is something, usually bad, that might happen

rock	rock is hard, consolidated material which is a part of the Earth's crust
roots	the parts of the plant that grow underground; roots hold the plant in place and absorb water and mineral salts
rot	to decay.
selective breeding	two organisms are chosen because of desirable characteristics and mated together to produce offspring, hopefully with a combination of the desired characteristics
sensation	a feeling
separate	to split apart
shock waves	waves of energy moving away from an event, e.g. an earthquake or an explosion
side-effect	an effect that happens but is not the main effect of the treatment; drugs can sometimes have side effects which do not always help the body even though the main effect is to cure the illness
solar kettles	a device that uses energy in sunlight to boil water
solar system	the collection of nine planets and other objects orbiting around the Sun
soluble	a soluble substance can dissolve in a liquid, e.g. sugar is soluble in water
solvent	the liquid that dissolves a solute to make a solution
sound meter	a device to measure the loudness of a sound
spectrum	a spectrum forms when the mixture of wavelengths in white light are spread out
spin	to turn around quickly, e.g. a compact disc revolves inside the CD player so that the laser can read the information it contains
stems	the thin part of the plant that supports the leaves and other parts of the plant above ground
stereoscopic	vision using two eyes to produce two slightly different images; the brain mixes these images to produce a composite image that allows distances to be judged more accurately
sterilise	killing all of the organisms in an area, usually used to mean killing microorganisms
stimulus	something that happens to an organism that produces a response, e.g. a change in daylength can make some birds fly south
storage	to keep something to use later
stored energy	energy stored in food or other chemicals (e.g. coal, oil)
sun protection factor (SPF)	a measure of how much ultraviolet light a suncream screens from the sunlight; high SPFs give more protection than low SPFs
superbugs	microorganisms that are not killed by a range of different antibiotics
surface area	the area of a surface; surface area has a significant effect on the rate of many chemical reactions
taste	the flavour of food
taste buds	organs on the tongue that detect tastes
tectonic plates	sections of the Earth's crust that float on top of the mantle; plates are hundreds of miles across and move a few inches a year
temperature	a measure of how hot something is
tooth decay	when bacteria breakdown teeth and get into the soft inner area and cause pain

toxic	poisonous
transfer	to move from one place to another
transmitter	a device which gives out some form of energy or signal, usually used to mean a radio transmitter which broadcasts radio signals
tsunami	a giant wave caused by an underwater explosion or earthquake
tumour	a mass of tissue formed by the uncontrolled division of cells; these cells cannot carry out normal cell functions and may damage healthy cells by pushing against them
turbine	a device that converts movement in a fluid into circular movement, usually to drive a generator; turbines are essential parts of a windmill and a hydroelectric power plant
UKAEA	the United Kingdom Atomic Energy Authority which is responsible for making sure Britain's nuclear reactors are safe
ultra high frequency (UHF)	electromagnetic signals used to transmit television programmes
ultraviolet (UV)	a type of electromagnetic radiation just beyond the blue end of the visible spectrum; UV light carries more energy than visible light and can cause suntans
uranium	a radioactive metal used in nuclear power stations and bombs
vaccinations	vaccinations are specially-weakened microorganisms that your body can practise against; when the real one tries to get in you can destroy it before it makes you ill
vaccuum	no air; space contains a vacuum – there is no atmosphere between the planets
varieties	a variety of a plant is a particular type, e.g. Cox's Orange Pippin is a variety of apple, Maris Piper is a variety of potato
very high frequency (VHF)	electromagnetic signals used to transmit radio programmes
vibration	a regular movement when something moves a very small distance to-and-fro but keeps repeating the movement over and over again
vitamins	chemicals needed by the body in very small amounts to keep it healthy
volcano	a place where molten rock from below the Earth's crust comes out onto the surface
volume	the loudness of a sound; also the space taken up by something, e.g. the volume of a rucksack might be 22 litres
wavelength	the distance between two identical points on a wave
white blood cells	blood cells which help to destroy foreign bodies in the body
x-rays	electromagnetic radiation used by doctors to look inside a patient's body or to destroy some types of cancer cells